Campbell's 213 Lightning Rounds

By John P. Campbell

Campbell's High School/College Quiz Book (Revised Edition)

Campbell's Potpourri I of Quiz Bowl Questions

Campbell's Potpourri II of Quiz Bowl Questions (Revised Edition)

Campbell's Middle School Quiz Book #1

Campbell's Potpourri III of Quiz Bowl Questions

Campbell's Middle School Quiz Book #2

Campbell's Elementary School Quiz Book #1

Campbell's 2001 Quiz Questions

Campbell's Potpourri IV of Quiz Bowl Questions

Campbell's Middle School Quiz Book #3

The 500 Famous Quotations Quiz Book (Out of Print)

Campbell's 2002 Quiz Questions

Campbell's 210 Lightning Rounds

Campbell's 175 Lightning Rounds

Campbell's 2003 Quiz Questions

Campbell's 211 Lightning Rounds

Omniscience™: The Basic Game of Knowledge in Book Form

Campbell's 2004 Quiz Questions

Campbell's 212 Lightning Rounds

Campbell's Elementary School Quiz Book #2

Campbell's 176 Lightning Rounds

Campbell's 213 Lightning Rounds

Campbell's Mastering the Myths Quiz Book

Campbell's 213 Lightning Rounds

by John P. Campbell

PATRICK'S PRESS

Columbus, Georgia

Printed in the United States of America

CIP data suggested by the author

Campbell, John P., 1942-
Campbell's 213 Lightning Rounds

Includes index.
Summary: 213 sets of 10 rapid-response questions or identifications arranged by theme.
1. Questions and answers. [1. Questions and answers]
I. Title II. Title: *Campbell's 213 Lightning Rounds*
III. Title: *213 Lightning Rounds*
IV. Title: *Two Hundred and Thirteen Lightning Rounds*
AG195.C287R 2002 031'.02

ISBN (International Standard Book Number): 0-944322-19-0

First Edition
First Printing, October 1994
Second Printing, October 1998
Third Printing, September, 2002

ACKNOWLEDGEMENTS

I am once again very indebted to my editor Rinda Brewbaker for her editing ability and contributions to this work.

I appreciate the help of the following in checking this material: Mark Huber, Mona Crawford, Sonya Owens, and David Taggart. I also thank Kevin Keegan, Mariane McLeod, Michael Pollack, and Peter Urban and the Millburn High School Academic Quiz Bowl Team for their contributions, and Pam Coffield and Deborah Metivier for their help.

I want to thank my mother, Mrs. John Campbell, for her support.

I thank Cornerstone Images for its help in typesetting this material.

To

Those students whose speed and accuracy in 60-second competitions affirm the power of the human mind, and to Golda Meir, who said, “I must govern the clock, not be governed by it.”

Preface

I would like to thank Questions Unlimited and Chip Beall for creating the idea of lightning rounds, but I would like to recommend that the time be increased to 75 or 90 seconds, especially in mathematics, to allow those who will create future rounds more flexibility in developing themes.

Please note that the last 38 theme rounds are considered more difficult than the first 175.

John Campbell

Contents

JOHN CAMPBELL

THE WORD *SINGLE*

Identify each of the following concerning the word *single*.

1) Soviet leader who supposedly said during his rule of terror, "A single death is a tragedy; a million deaths is a statistic."
2) Only U.S. President to remain single
3) Possession mid-18th century French physiocrats believed was the single source of wealth
4) Odds in favor of rolling a "3" on a single toss of a fair die
5) In meiosis, number of daughter cells produced by a single cell
6) Last major presidential candidate to be single, a contender in both 1952 and 1956
7) Geometric term used to describe 3 or more lines that intersect at a single point
8) Object suspended by a single thread over the head of Damocles to illustrate the threat of impending danger
9) Single landmass that split apart about 200 million years ago to form Gondwana and Laurasia
10) Gymnosperm that is the single surviving species of an order that flourished at the time of the dinosaurs

Answers:

1) Joseph Stalin
2) James Buchanan
3) Land
4) 1 to 5 (NOTE: 1 out of 6 is the probability of tossing a "3" but it is incorrect because the question specifies "odds")
5) 4
6) Adlai Stevenson
7) Concurrent
8) Sword (of Damocles)
9) Pangaea (or Pangea)
10) *Ginkgoales* (*ginkgoaceae*), or ginkgo (accept maiden-hair tree)

COMPLETION OF OPERA TITLES

Complete the title of each of the following operas.

1) *Madama* _________
2) *Porgy and* _________
3) *The Flying* _________
4) *Pelléas and* _________
5) *Orpheus and* _________
6) *Amahl and the* _________
7) *Hansel and* _________
8) *Samson and* _________
9) *Così* _________
10) *Tristan und* _________

Answers:

1) *Butterfly*
2) *Bess*
3) *Dutchman*
4) *Mélisande*
5) *Eurydice*
6) *Night Visitors*
7) *Gretel*
8) *Delilah* (or *Dalila*)
9) *Fan Tutte*
10) *Isolde*

U.S. PRESIDENTIAL ELECTION YEARS

Identify the year of each of the following from the given information.

1) Republicans Nixon and Agnew defeated Democrats McGovern and Shriver
2) Republicans Hoover and Curtis defeated Democrats Smith and Robinson
3) Democrats Johnson and Humphrey defeated Republicans Goldwater and Miller
4) Whigs Taylor and Fillmore defeated Democrats Cass and Butler
5) Republicans Lincoln and Johnson defeated Democrats McClellan and Pendleton
6) Republicans Grant and Wilson defeated Democratic-Liberal Republicans Greeley and Brown
7) Republicans Reagan and Bush defeated Democrats Mondale and Ferraro
8) Democrats Kennedy and Johnson defeated Republicans Nixon and Lodge
9) Democrats Cleveland and Stevenson defeated Republicans Harrison and Reid
10) Republicans Hayes and Wheeler defeated Democrats Tilden and Hendricks

Answers:

1) 1972
2) 1928
3) 1964
4) 1848
5) 1864
6) 1872
7) 1984
8) 1960
9) 1892
10) 1876

20TH CENTURY FICTIONAL CHARACTERS

Complete the name of the following 20th century fictional characters.

1) George Lucas' Darth _________
2) Margaret Mitchell's Scarlett _________
3) T.S. Eliot's J. Alfred _________
4) Sinclair Lewis' George F. _________
5) J.D. Salinger's Holden _________
6) Richard Wright's Bigger _________
7) William Faulkner's Benjy _________
8) Truman Capote's Holly _________
9) Harper Lee's Atticus _________
10) H.T. Webster's Caspar _________

Answers:

1) Vader
2) O'Hara
3) Prufrock
4) Babbitt
5) Caulfield
6) Thomas
7) Compson
8) Golightly
9) Finch
10) Milquetoast

THE LETTER *V*

Identify each of the following by giving an answer that includes the letter *V*.

1) Zachary Taylor's victorious Mexican battle site whose name means "Good View"
2) Smallest Central American country in area
3) Last book of the Bible
4) U.S. President who said, "Yesterday, December 7, 1941—a date which will live in infamy . . . ."
5) Russian composer of *Peter and the Wolf*
6) In *Hamlet*, what Shakespeare said is "the soul of wit"
7) Country whose capital is Caracas
8) Kind of bond consisting of pairs of shared electrons
9) Neck, especially the back of the neck, as well as part of the uterus
10) Russian composer of *The Firebird*

Answers:

1) Buena Vista
2) El Salvador
3) Revelation
4) (Franklin) Roosevelt
5) (Sergei) Prokofiev
6) Brevity
7) Venezuela
8) Covalent
9) Cervix
10) (Igor) Stravinsky

HUMAN ANATOMY

Identify each of the following as belonging to the "head," the "torso," or the "extremities."

1) Biceps
2) Cerebellum
3) Pancreas
4) Ilium
5) Cochlea
6) Duodenum
7) Patella
8) Vena cava
9) Sartorius
10) Adenoids

Answers:

1) Extremities
2) Head
3) Torso
4) Torso
5) Head
6) Torso
7) Extremities
8) Torso
9) Extremities
10) Head

QUICK MATH

Answer each of the following quick math questions.

1) If a person runs a mile in 4 minutes, how many miles will he run in 3 hours at the same pace?
2) What number increased by 30% of itself equals 39?
3) Which geometric solid contains a maximum volume for a given surface area?
4) What property of addition is illustrated by the equality $7 + 2 = 2 + 7$?
5) By what geometric name do we know the graph of the equation: *y equals x plus 1*?
6) What is the cube root of the positive square root of 64?
7) What is the next consecutive prime number after 97?
8) What is the formula for finding the area of a circle?
9) Which property in algebra justifies that c times the sum of x and y equals cx plus cy?
10) Which theorem states that for any right triangle the sum of the squares of the legs is equal to the square of the hypotenuse?

Answers:

1) 45 miles (accept 45)
2) 30
3) Sphere
4) Commutative Property (of addition)
5) Line or straight line
6) 2
7) 101
8) Area = πr^2 (accept *pi r* squared; area equals *pi* radius squared)
9) Distributive
10) Pythagorean (theorem)

20TH CENTURY PEOPLE

Complete the name of each of the following famous 20th century people.

1) Spanish artist Salvador _________
2) British politician Neville _________
3) Producer and director George M. _________
4) Russian ballet star Vaslav _________
5) English nurse Edith Louisa _________
6) Singer Elvis Aron _________
7) Actor Edward G. _________
8) Teamster leader James Riddle _________
9) Baseball player George Herman _________
10) Artist Georgia _________

Answers:

1) Dali
2) Chamberlain
3) Cohan
4) Nijinsky
5) Cavell
6) Presley
7) Robinson
8) Hoffa
9) Ruth
10) O'Keeffe

AMERICAN CREATORS OF LITERARY CHARACTERS

Identify the American author who created each of the following characters.

1) Amy March
2) Henry Fleming
3) Natty Bumppo
4) Jay Gatsby
5) Wang Lung
6) Yossarian
7) Ichabod Crane
8) John Proctor
9) Ashley Wilkes
10) Nurse Ratched

Answers:

1) Louisa May Alcott
2) Stephen Crane
3) James Fenimore Cooper
4) F. Scott Fitzgerald
5) Pearl Buck
6) Joseph Heller
7) Washington Irving
8) Arthur Miller
9) Margaret Mitchell
10) Ken Kesey

LEGISLATIVE ACTS

Identify each of the following legislative acts.

1) 1765 act designed to raise funds for the British army stationed in America
2) 1807 act closing U.S. ports to all foreign ships and known humorously as the "O-Grab-Me" Act
3) 1883 act establishing the principle of federal employment based on merit and competitive examination
4) 1887 act requiring American Indians to give up their tribal lands in return for citizenship
5) 1919 act providing for enforcement of national prohibition of liquors
6) 1941 act permitting the President to transfer weapons and other supplies to any nation
7) 1964 act banning discrimination because of color, race, national origin, religion, or sex
8) 1973 act requiring the President to inform Congress within 48 hours before deploying troops into hostile areas
9) Acronym for the social security tax shared equally by employers and workers
10) Word represented by *R* in RICO, the act allowing the government to freeze assets suspected of being illegally acquired

Answers:

1) Stamp Act
2) Embargo Act
3) Pendleton Act (or Pendleton Civil Service Act)
4) Dawes Act
5) Volstead Act
6) Lend-Lease Act
7) Civil Rights Act (of 1964)
8) War Powers Act (or Resolution)
9) FICA (Federal Insurance Contributions Act)
10) Racketeer (Influenced and Corrupt Organizations Act)

THE WORD *PRINCE*

Identify the following, each of which is associated with the word *prince.*

1) English poet, sometimes called the "Prince of Poets," who authored *Samson Agonistes* and went blind at age 43
2) Country whose capital is Port-au-Prince
3) Italian author of *The Prince*, a 1513 political treatise
4) Exxon ship that spilled gallons of oil in Prince William Sound in 1989
5) Shakespearean play subtitled the *Prince of Denmark*
6) Egyptian god slain by his evil brother Seth and known as the Prince of the Dead
7) Principality headed by Prince Rainier III
8) Author of *The Prince of Tides*, a book describing life in South Carolina
9) Canadian province that is the setting for *Anne of Green Gables*
10) Grand Prince who became a Christian about 989 and converted many Russians to Christianity

Answers:

1) John Milton
2) Haiti
3) Niccolò Machiavelli
4) *Exxon Valdez*
5) *Hamlet*
6) Osiris
7) Monaco
8) Pat Conroy
9) Prince Edward Island
10) Vladimir (I; the Great or Saint Vladimir)

THE LETTER *W*

Identify each of the following by giving an answer that includes the letter *W*.

1) Novel that includes the line, "This here is William James Joad, dyed of a stroke, old, old man."
2) Leader whose Domesday Book is a Latin record of a census and survey of England
3) Country whose capital is Bern
4) U.S. state known as the "Garden State"
5) U.N. country whose name is last alphabetically
6) Englishman known for *Origin of Species*
7) Plant whose name means "noble white" in German
8) U.S. Vice President who resigned his office
9) English author of *Sonnets From the Portuguese*
10) Landlocked province of Canada whose capital is Regina

Answers:

1) *The Grapes of Wrath*
2) William (the Conqueror; made in 1086)
3) Switzerland
4) New Jersey
5) Zimbabwe
6) Charles Darwin
7) Edelweiss
8) Spiro Agnew (accept John Caldwell Calhoun if the middle name is given)
9) Elizabeth Barrett Browning
10) Saskatchewan

CLASSES OF ANIMALS

Identify the class to which the following animals belong.

1) Fishes, in general (superclass)
2) Frogs
3) Horses
4) Humans
5) Kangaroos
6) Lobsters and crabs
7) Octopuses and squids
8) Spiders
9) Sharks
10) Sea Urchins

Answer:

1) Pisces
2) Amphibia (amphibians)
3) Mammalia (mammals)
4) Mammalia (mammals)
5) Mammalia (mammals)
6) Mala costraca (accept crustacea or crustacean)
7) Cephalopoda (cephalopod)
8) Arachnida (arachnids)
9) Chondichtyes (accept pisces)
10) Echinoidea (echinoid)

QUICK MATH

Answer each of the following quick math questions.

1) At $1.50 per gallon, what would be the cost of gasoline for a 300-mile trip in an automobile that averages 15 miles to the gallon?
2) What is the value for the geometric mean of 2 and 18?
3) How many degrees are in the smaller angle formed by the hands of a clock at 8 o'clock?
4) What is the largest positive 3-digit multiple of 3?
5) What integer does the fifth root of negative 32 equal?
6) What is the sum in degrees of the measures of the interior angles of a convex pentagon?
7) What is the principal square root of 289?
8) What is the logarithm of 25 to the base 5?
9) What real number is equal to the square of the number i?
10) If 5 inches on a map represent 100 miles, how many inches on the map represent 160 miles?

Answers:

1) $30
2) 6 (do NOT accept –6)
3) 120 (degrees)
4) 999
5) Negative 2
6) 540 (degrees)
7) 17
8) 2
9) –1 (negative one)
10) 8 (inches)

FATHERLY NICKNAMES OF LITERARY EUROPEANS

Identify the following literary Europeans, each of whom is known by a nickname including the word "Father."

1) French "Father of Science Fiction" and author of *Voyage to the Center of the Earth*
2) German "Founder and Father of Modern Communism" and author of *Das Kapital*
3) English "Father of Modern Prose Fiction" and author of *Robinson Crusoe*
4) "Father of English Poetry" and author of *The Canterbury Tales*
5) "Father of English Inductive Philosophy" and author of the *Advancement of Learning*
6) English "Father of Philosophy" and author of *Opus majus*
7) "Father of French Tragedy" and author of *Le Cid*
8) French "Father of Ridicule" and author of *Gargantua* and *Pantagruel*
9) "Father of the English Novel" and author of *Tom Jones*
10) French "Father of Modern Philosophy" and author of *Discours de la Méthode* (*Discourse on Method*)

Answers:

1) Jules Verne
2) Karl Marx
3) Daniel Defoe
4) Geoffrey Chaucer
5) Francis Bacon
6) Roger Bacon
7) Pierre Corneille
8) Francois Rabelais
9) Henry Fielding
10) René Descartes

FAMOUS PEOPLE WITH THE SAME SURNAMES

Identify the surname shared by all three famous people in the following groups.

1) Miles, Bette, Jefferson
2) Michael, Shirley, Stonewall
3) Byron Raymond, E.B., Margaret Bourke
4) Magic, Samuel, James Weldon
5) Howard, Charles Evans, Langston
6) Bobby, Inigo, John Paul
7) John Moses, Robert, Elizabeth Barrett
8) Marshall, Eugene, Cyrus West
9) William, Evangeline Cory, John Wilkes
10) John, Edmund G., Charles Brockden

Answers:

1) Davis
2) Jackson
3) White
4) Johnson
5) Hughes
6) Jones
7) Browning
8) Field
9) Booth
10) Brown

BAYS, GULFS, AND SOUNDS

Identify the following bays, gulfs, and sounds.

1) Bay, bounded by Manitoba, Ontario, and Quebec and connected with the Atlantic Ocean by a strait of the same name
2) Atlantic Ocean bay near Miami, Florida
3) Pacific Ocean Gulf between Baja California and the mainland of Mexico
4) Atlantic Ocean bay between Maryland and Virginia
5) Gulf bounded by the U.S., Cuba, and Mexico
6) Atlantic Ocean bay in Canada renowned for its record breaking tides
7) Gulf connected with the Gulf of Oman and Arabian Sea through the Strait of Hormuz
8) Bay that is the site of U.S. naval base in Cuba
9) Pacific Ocean sound that curves deep into Washington state
10) South Pacific Ocean bay south of Sydney

Answers:

1) Hudson Bay
2) Biscayne Bay
3) Gulf of California (sometimes called the Sea of Cortés)
4) Chesapeake Bay
5) Gulf of Mexico
6) Bay of Fundy (accept Ungava Bay)
7) Persian Gulf
8) Guantánamo Bay
9) Puget Sound
10) Botany Bay

RELIGIOUS WORKS

Identify the following world-renowned religious books or works.

1) Compilation of maxims, aphorisms, and discourses of Confucius from the 5th-6th centuries B.C.
2) Hebrew name meaning "law" for the first 5 books of the Bible
3) Greek word meaning "five books" or "five scrolls" or the first 5 books of the Bible
4) Collective name for the first 4 books of the New Testament
5) Entire body of Hindu sacred writings
6) Sacred text of Islam
7) Chinese "Book of Changes"
8) Prayer book of the Anglicans
9) Sacred book discovered and translated by Joseph Smith
10) St. Jerome's 4th Century Latin version of the Bible

Answer:

1) *The Analects* (or *The Analects of Confucius*)
2) Torah
3) Pentateuch
4) The Gospels
5) Vedas (accept Veda; accept Samhita)
6) Koran (or Qur'an)
7) *I Ching*
8) *Book of Common Prayer*
9) *Book of Mormon*
10) Vulgate

THE LETTER *X*

Identify each of the following by giving an answer that includes the letter *X*.

1) Term in chemistry for a product of 2 or more substances not chemically combined
2) U.S. President who said, "I want you all to stonewall it."
3) Name for the trunk of an insect
4) Priest known as "The Apostle of the Scottish Reformation"
5) Body system of which the kidneys are a part
6) Capital of Nova Scotia
7) Author of *Brave New World*
8) Collection of dust, gas, and stars thousands of light years in diameter
9) Emperor of Mexico executed in 1867
10) Ballet for 2 dancers

Answers:

1) Mixture
2) Richard Nixon
3) Thorax
4) John Knox
5) Excretory
6) Halifax
7) Aldous Huxley
8) Galaxy
9) Maximilian
10) Pas de deux

ASTRONOMY

Identify each of the following terms used in astronomy.

1) Complete or partial blocking of light from one celestial body by another
2) Moon or satellite's point of orbit farthest from the earth
3) Celestial body composed of a dense nucleus of frozen gases, ice, and rock
4) Cloud of gas-and-dust remains in interstellar space
5) Aurora in the Northern Hemisphere; "Northern Lights"
6) Theoretical explosion that began the universe
7) Star that explodes
8) Bands of high radiation circling the earth
9) Moon or satellite's orbit point nearest to the Earth
10) Celestial sources of variable radio signals

Answer:

1) Eclipse
2) Apogee
3) Comet
4) Nebula
5) Aurora Borealis
6) Big Bang
7) Supernova (accept nova)
8) Van Allen Belts
9) Perigee
10) Pulsar

GEOGRAPHY

Identify each of the following places.

1) Island that forms the southeastern part of New York City and has a greater population than that of 41 of the 50 states
2) U.S. island with the largest area
3) U.S. state known as the "Land of the Midnight Sun"
4) U.S. state capital located on the southern tip of Puget Sound
5) Island state of the Australian Commonwealth
6) U.S. city known for the Steel Curtain defense of its NFL team and nicknamed the "Steel City"
7) U.S. state in which Dartmouth College is located
8) U.S. state that is the site of President James Madison's home, Montpelier
9) Largest island in the Mediterranean, an autonomous region of Italy
10) Europe's 2nd largest island in area

Answers:

1) Long Island
2) Hawaii
3) Alaska
4) Olympia (Washington)
5) Tasmania
6) Pittsburgh
7) New Hampshire
8) Virginia
9) Sicily
10) Iceland

JAPAN

Identify each of the following concerning Japan and its culture.

1) Japanese form of wrestling usually involving very sizable men
2) One-engine WWII fighter plane
3) Its most famous volcano, the highest point in Japan
4) Form of Buddhism emphasizing enlightenment through meditation
5) Title for the emperor used to name a Gilbert and Sullivan operetta
6) Its legislature
7) Loose, wide-sleeve robe fastened at the waist by a sash
8) Sash for this loose, wide-sleeve robe
9) Fermented, slightly alcoholic wine made from rice
10) Cold boiled rice topped with raw seafood

Answers:

1) Sumo
2) Zero
3) Mount Fuji (or Fujiyama)
4) Zen
5) Mikado
6) Diet
7) Kimono
8) Obi
9) Sake
10) Sushi

HISTORY

Identify each of the following concerning major historical events.

1) Chief justice of the U.S. Supreme Court who headed the investigation of the assassination of President Kennedy
2) Man sculpted on Georgia's Stone Mountain who died during the Civil War
3) Icelandic explorer credited with the discovery of North America in A.D. 1000
4) Name given to the ruling group formed by Pompey, Julius Caesar, and Marcus Crassus
5) Year William the Conqueror defeated King Harold in the Battle of Hastings
6) Explorer who became in 1513 the first European to see the eastern shore of the Pacific Ocean
7) Person who succeeded to the presidency following the death of William McKinley
8) English King who separated the Church of England from the Roman Catholic Church
9) Present-day U.S. state in which Lt. Col. George Custer made his last stand at Little Bighorn in 1876
10) American colonial governor who purchased Manhattan Island from the Indians in 1626 for about $24

Answers:

1) Earl Warren (Warren Commission Report)
2) Thomas "Stonewall" Jackson
3) Leif Eriksson (Erikson)
4) First Triumvirate (accept Triumvirate)
5) 1066
6) Vasco Núñez de Balboa
7) Theodore Roosevelt
8) Henry VIII
9) Montana
10) Peter Minuit

FAMOUS ROBERTS

Identify each of the following famous Roberts.

1) Son of a President and U.S. Republican senator from Ohio who lost 3 presidential bids, in 1940, in 1948, and in 1952
2) "Father of the Space Age" who launched the first liquid-fueled rocket in 1926
3) Scottish poet who wrote "Auld Lang Syne"
4) Poet who wrote "To the Virgins, to Make Much of Time"
5) Inventor of the *Clermont*, the first commercially successful steamboat
6) British poet whose dramatic monologues are collected in *Dramatis Personae*
7) Confederate leader who became president of Washington College in Virginia
8) English explorer who led 2 expeditions to Antarctica
9) Hemingway's main character in *For Whom the Bell Tolls*
10) Cleveland Indian pitcher called "Rapid Robert" who won 266 games and threw 12 one-hitters

Answers:

1) Robert Taft
2) Robert Goddard
3) Robert Burns
4) Robert Herrick
5) Robert Fulton
6) Robert Browning
7) Robert E. Lee
8) Robert Falcon Scott
9) Robert Jordan
10) Robert Feller

MUSIC TERMS

Identify each of the following terms used in music.

1) Method of composition based on a chromatic scale of 12 developed by Arnold Schoenberg
2) Highest female voice
3) Gradual increase in volume
4) Extended vocal solo in an opera or oratorio
5) Five horizontal lines on and between which notes are written
6) Sonata for orchestra, usually in four movements
7) Character that indicates the pitch of a particular line on a stave
8) Lowest male voice
9) Combination of three or more tones played at once
10) Direction to play very softly

Answers:

1) Twelve-tone music (dodecaphonic)
2) Soprano
3) Crescendo
4) Aria
5) Staff (accept stave)
6) Symphony
7) Clef
8) Bass
9) Chord
10) Pianissimo

THE LETTER *Y*

Identify each of the following by giving an answer that ends in the letter *Y*.

1) Concentration of a solution expressed as the number of moles of solute in a liter of solution
2) Cranial nerve that carries the sensation of smell from the nose to the brain
3) Body system of which the throat is a part
4) Englishman who discovered that blood circulates in the human body
5) American credited with saying, “Go West, young man, and grow up with the country”
6) Tendency of the surface of a liquid to rise or fall when in contact with very small diameter tubes
7) Ancient city discovered by Heinrich Schliemann
8) Third U.S. President to be assassinated
9) Russian author of *Crime and Punishment*
10) Mississippi woman who wrote *The Optimist’s Daughter*

Answers:

1) Molarity
2) Olfactory (nerve)
3) Respiratory
4) (William) Harvey
5) (Horace) Greeley
6) Capillarity (accept capillary action or attraction)
7) Troy
8) (William) McKinley
9) (Fyodor) Dostoyevsky
10) (Eudora) Welty

COLORS

Name the basic color associated with each of the following shades.

1) Azure
2) Crimson
3) Saffron
4) Sable
5) Flaxen
6) Grizzled
7) Mauve
8) Sepia
9) Magenta
10) Vermilion

Answers:

1) Blue
2) Red
3) Yellow (accept orange)
4) Black (accept brown)
5) Yellow
6) Gray (accept brown, as in brown fur)
7) Purple
8) Brown
9) Purple (accept red)
10) Red (accept orange)

QUICK MATH

Identify each of the following.

1) Of complementary, supplementary, and obtuse, word for the relationship between consecutive angles of a rhombus
2) Point of intersection of two consecutive sides of a polygon
3) Polynomial with two terms
4) Period of the sine function
5) Value of the cosine of 0 degrees
6) Conjugate of 1 plus *i*
7) Numerical value of 6 times *m* to the zero power all divided by 2, if *m* is not equal to zero
8) Integer that is two-seventeenths of 51
9) Slope of the line with equation $y = -2x + 4$ (y equals negative two *x* plus four)
10) Given a circle in a plane, locus of the midpoints of all the diameters of the circle

Answers:

1) Supplementary
2) Vertex
3) Binomial
4) 2 *pi* (accept 360 degrees)
5) 1
6) One minus *i*
7) 3
8) 6
9) –2 (negative two)
10) Point (this point is the center of the circle)

AFRICAN HISTORY

Identify each of the following people associated with African history.

1) Last of the Ptolemaic line, linked with Caesar and Antony
2) Said, "Dr. Livingstone, I presume," in 1871
3) Resisted the Italian invasion of Ethiopia in 1935
4) General who crossed the Alps with elephants to attack Rome in the 3rd century B.C.
5) Builder of the largest of Giza's 3 great pyramids
6) 13th century B.C. Egyptian "king of kings"
7) Carthaginian queen and lover of Aeneas
8) Pharaoh who built the Step Pyramid at Sakkara
9) Akhenaton's chief wife
10) Hannibal's father, who led the Sicilian Army in the First Punic War

Answer:

1) Cleopatra (VII Philopator)
2) Henry Stanley
3) Haile Selassie
4) Hannibal
5) Cheops or Khufu
6) Ramses (II)
7) Dido or Elissa
8) Zoser (Djoser, etc.)
9) Nefertiti
10) Hamilcar (accept Hamilcar Barca)

FOREIGN WORDS AND PHRASES

Give the foreign word or phrase beginning with the given letter for each of the following.

1) P - "Truth" in Russian, or the name of the Communist Party newspaper
2) C - "That's life" in French
3) K - "Fate" in Turkish, or the title of a Broadway musical
4) A - "Goodbye" in Italian
5) S - "Always Faithful" in Latin for the U.S. Marine Corps motto
6) S - "Peace" in Hebrew
7) S - "Peace" in Arabic
8) K - "Good day" in Japanese
9) H - "the masses" in Greek
10) H - "Modern" in Korean, or the name of an automobile company

Answers:

1) Pravda
2) C'est la vie
3) Kismet
4) Arrivederci
5) Semper fidelis (accept semper fi)
6) Shalom
7) Salaam
8) Konnichi-wa
9) Hoi polloi
10) Hyundai

AMERICAN POETS AND THEIR POEMS

Identify the American poet who wrote each of the following poems.

1) "The Raven"
2) "The Death of the Hired Man"
3) "Concord Hymn"
4) "When Lilacs Last in the Dooryard Bloom'd"
5) "Trees"
6) "The Love Song of J. Alfred Prufrock"
7) "Barbara Frietchie"
8) "The Song of the Chattahoochee"
9) "Thanatopsis"
10) "Richard Cory"

Answers:

1) Edgar Allan Poe
2) Robert Frost
3) Ralph Waldo Emerson
4) Walt Whitman
5) Joyce Kilmer
6) T.S. Eliot
7) John Greenleaf Whittier
8) Sidney Lanier
9) William Cullen Bryant
10) Edwin Arlington Robinson

FAMOUS PEOPLE ASSOCIATED WITH CANADA

Identify each of the following famous people associated with Canada.

1) Prime Minister who won the 1957 Nobel Peace Prize for organizing U.N. intervention in 1956 Suez Crisis
2) Author of *Anne of Green Gables*
3) Inventor of basketball
4) Author of *The Medium is the Message: An Inventory of Effects*
5) First female prime minister
6) Explorer and mapmaker after whom island and city in British Columbia are named
7) Explorer often called "Father of New France"
8) Explorer who was the first European to cross North America north of Mexico overland
9) "Poet of the Yukon" and author of *Songs of a Sourdough*
10) Author of *Never Cry Wolf* and *Woman in the Mists: The Story of Dian Fossey and the Mountain Gorillas of Africa*

Answers:

1) Lester B. Pearson
2) Lucy Maud Montgomery
3) James Naismith
4) Marshall McLuhan (written with Quentin Fiore)
5) Kim Campbell
6) George Vancouver
7) Samuel de Champlain
8) Sir Alexander Mackenzie
9) Robert Service
10) Farley Mowat

THE LETTER *Z*

Identify each of the following by giving an answer that includes the letter *Z*.

1) Last element alphabetically on the periodic table, whose atomic number is 40
2) American author of *This Side of Paradise*
3) English meaning of the French *hors d'oeuvre*
4) River that carries more water than any other
5) To hypnotize, derived from the name of an Austrian physician who stared into patients' eyes
6) One of Hamlet's 2 friends who was commissioned by the king to spy on him
7) Discoverer of electromagnetic waves
8) Heavily armored WWII German tank
9) American ship rescued in Cambodia during the Ford administration
10) Former capital of the Philippines located on the island of Luzon

Answers:

1) Zirconium
2) F. Scott Fitzgerald
3) Appetizer
4) Amazon River
5) Mesmerize (Franz Mesmer)
6) Rosencrantz
7) Heinrich Hertz
8) Panzer
9) *Mayagüez*
10) Quezon City (accept Quezon)

LUNGS AND BREATHING

Identify each of the following terms concerning lungs and breathing.

1) Dome-shaped breathing muscle that separates the abdominal and chest cavities
2) Voice box
3) Windpipe
4) Adjective meaning "pertaining to the lungs"
5) Waste gas released from the lungs that is exchanged for oxygen from the air
6) Tube connecting the mouth and the stomach, lying between the 2 lungs
7) Sticky fluid that lines the air passageways and traps foreign substances
8) Tube that connects the mouth with the esophagus
9) Two smaller tubes into which the windpipe divides
10) Tiny air sac in the lungs in which oxygen is transferred to the blood

Answers:

1) Diaphragm
2) Larynx
3) Trachea
4) Pulmonary
5) Carbon dioxide
6) Esophagus
7) Mucus
8) Pharynx (accept fauces)
9) Bronchi
10) Alveolus

QUICK MATH

Answer each of the following quick math questions.

1) Which of the following is most closely associated with the term "discriminant": Binomial Theorem, Pythagorean Theorem, or Quadratic Formula?
2) If a square of side 2 has been circumscribed about a circle, what is the circle's circumference?
3) Over the set of real numbers, which of the 3 conic sections is a discontinuous curve?
4) What is the geometric mean of 3 and 5?
5) About which of the following is the cosine function symmetric: x-axis, y-axis, or origin?
6) Of odd, even, or neither, which one describes the sine function?
7) How many lines of symmetry does a square have?
8) What is the mathematical name for the set of all points satisfying a given geometrical condition?
9) How many yards are there in a furlong, or in 1/8 of a mile?
10) How many subsets can be formed from a set with 5 distinct elements?

Answers:

1) Quadratic Formula
2) 2 *pi*
3) Hyperbola
4) Square root of 15
5) Y-axis
6) Odd
7) 4
8) Locus
9) 220
10) 32 (accept 2 to the fifth power)

U.S. HISTORY

Identify each of the following concerning U.S. history.

1) First U.S. Vice President to become President
2) Famous aviator known as "The Lone Eagle"
3) WWII general remembered for saying, "I shall return"
4) War ended by the Treaty of Ghent
5) Largest Confederate military prison during the Civil War
6) American frontiersman known as "Wild Bill"
7) President who in 1823 warned European powers to stay out of the Americas
8) President who made his Fourteen Points Address in 1918
9) Congressman from Nebraska who made his "Cross of Gold" speech in 1896
10) First astronaut to orbit the Earth

Answers:

1) John Adams
2) Charles Lindbergh
3) Douglas MacArthur
4) War of 1812
5) Andersonville
6) (James Butler) Hickok
7) James Monroe (Monroe Doctrine)
8) Woodrow Wilson
9) William Jennings Bryan
10) John Glenn

DOUBLE *T*

Identify the following by giving an answer that includes a double *t*.

1) Word used to describe hard substances that are easily broken
2) Author of the novel *Little Women*
3) Eli Whitney invention
4) U.S. capital city
5) U.S. general nicknamed "Old Blood and Guts"
6) Asian city famous for its "Black Hole"
7) July 1-3, 1863, Civil War battle
8) New England state
9) Bacteria causing typhus
10) Empire whose name is often used interchangeably with the word "Turkey"

Answers:

1) Brittle
2) (Louisa May) Alcott
3) Cotton gin
4) Little Rock
5) (George) Patton
6) Calcutta
7) Gettysburg
8) Massachusetts
9) Rickettsia
10) Ottoman (Empire)

U.S. CONSTITUTION

Identify each of the following concerning the U.S. Constitution.

1) Year Constitution was signed on September 17
2) City in which the Constitution was signed by 39 delegates
3) Name for its first 10 Amendments
4) Number of its Articles
5) Number of successful amendments since 1793
6) Virginian known as "The Father of the Constitution"
7) Fraction of state legislatures that must ratify an amendment for it to be adopted
8) Number of states needed for ratification of the Constitution
9) Washington, D.C., site where the original copy of the document is preserved
10) State that refused to send representatives to the Constitutional Convention

Answers:

1) 1787
2) Philadelphia
3) Bill of Rights
4) 7
5) 16 (accept 17; the 27th Amendment may need court approval)
6) James Madison
7) 3/4
8) 9
9) National Archives Building (accept National Archives)
10) Rhode Island

THE WORD *TABLE*

Identify each of the following concerning the word *table*.

1) Latin word for "table" that names an organization for people with IQ's in the top 2% of the general population
2) Russian chemist considered responsible for devising a Periodic Table of Elements
3) Site where King Arthur had his Round Table
4) Chemical term for table sugar
5) With 5 guests for dinner, number of ways a host can arrange the guests at a circular dinner table
6) Book whose text Joseph Smith allegedly transcribed from Golden tablets or tables
7) Sport more commonly called "ping pong"
8) Chemical term for table salt
9) Spanish word for "table" that designates a flat, table-like upland, which falls away steeply on all sides
10) English scientist who formulated the law of partial pressures and produced the first table of atomic weights

Answers:

1) Mensa
2) Dmitri Mendeleev (or Mendeleyev)
3) Camelot
4) Sucrose
5) 24
6) Book of Mormon
7) Table tennis
8) Sodium chloride
9) Mesa
10) John Dalton

THE LETTER *Q*

Identify each of the following by giving an answer that includes the letter *Q*.

1) Time when the sun crosses the equator, making night and day of equal length
2) Court of the Roman Catholic Church that convened in the Middle Ages to suppress heresy
3) Adjective describing a surface through which light cannot pass
4) Cephalopod sea mollusk having 8 arms and 2 long tentacles
5) Country in which the Shatt-al-Arab waterway enters the Persian Gulf
6) Caribbean country where Mont Pelée is located
7) Largest city of New Mexico
8) Art of riding on horseback
9) Capital of Ecuador
10) Evenness of mind or temper; composure

Answers:

1) Equinox
2) Inquisition
3) Opaque
4) Squid
5) Iraq
6) Martinique
7) Albuquerque
8) Equitation
9) Quito
10) Equanimity (accept equanimous)

DIGESTIVE SYSTEM

Identify each of the following concerning the digestive system.

1) Part between stomach and the colon that absorbs nutrients through tiny blood and lymph vessels in its walls
2) Tube that extends from the mouth to the rectum
3) Clear digestive fluid secreted by glands in the lining of the stomach
4) Part of the small intestine between the duodenum and the ileum
5) Greenish-yellow substance produced by the liver that aids digestion in the duodenum
6) One of the 4 enzymes in the pancreatic juice
7) Last and largest section of the tube that extends from the mouth to the rectum
8) Digestive enzyme secreted by the stomach that is the chief enzyme of gastric juice
9) Partly digested food in the stomach that has been changed to a thick liquid
10) Enzyme in the saliva that changes starches in the food to sugar

Answers:

1) Small intestine
2) Alimentary canal or tract (accept gastrointestinal tract)
3) Gastric juice
4) Jejunum
5) Bile (accept gall)
6) Amylase, lipase, trypsin, or peptidase
7) Large intestine
8) Pepsin
9) Chyme
10) Ptyalin (accept amylase)

INFLUENTIAL WOMEN OF THE 20TH CENTURY

Identify each of the following concerning influential women of the 20th century.

1) Alabama woman whose refusal to give up her bus seat led to a Supreme Court decision declaring racial segregation unconstitutional
2) Anthropologist who studied family structure in Samoa
3) Blind and deaf Radcliffe graduate who brought worldwide attention to needs of the physically handicapped
4) First Lady who wrote a syndicated daily column called "My Day," and who worked for women's rights, minorities, and the poor
5) Founder of National Organization for Women (NOW) and author of *The Feminine Mystique*
6) Artist whose paintings are marked by organic abstract forms and Southwestern U.S. motifs as in her work *Summer Days*
7) American impressionistic painter of home life scenes, including *The Bath*
8) First American woman to win a Nobel Prize for literature, in 1938
9) First woman to win a Pulitzer Prize for fiction, in 1921
10) Founder of the American Birth Control League, later renamed Planned Parenthood

Answers:

1) Rosa Parks
2) Margaret Mead
3) Helen Keller
4) Eleanor Roosevelt
5) Betty Friedan
6) Georgia O'Keeffe
7) Mary Cassatt (she died in 1926 but had virtually stopped working by 1914)
8) Pearl S. Buck
9) Edith Wharton
10) Margaret Sanger

THE WORD *PRINCE*

Identify the following, each of which is associated with the word *prince*.

1) Grimm fairy tale character transformed by a witch but turned back into a prince as a favor to a princess
2) Country of Prince Henry, known as the "Father of Navigation"
3) French author of *The Little Prince*
4) Capital of Prince Edward Island
5) Tchaikovsky ballet involving Prince Siegfried and the evil magician Rothbart
6) Edgar Allan Poe 1842 short story of death featuring Prince Prospero
7) European capital in which Twain's *The Prince and the Pauper* is set
8) Prince of Norway in Shakespeare's *Hamlet*
9) U.S. state in which Princeton University is located
10) 14th century Prince of Wales and Duke of Cornwall known as "The Black Prince"

Answers:

1) Frog prince (accept frog as the word *prince* is in the question)
2) Portugal
3) Antoine de Saint-Exupéry
4) Charlottetown
5) *Swan Lake*
6) "The Masque of the Red Death"
7) London
8) Fortinbras
9) New Jersey
10) Edward

FAMOUS ROBERTS

Identify each of the following famous Roberts.

1) Physicist who formulated the law that the volume of a gas at constant temperature varies inversely to the pressure applied to the gas
2) Scottish author of *The Strange Case of Dr. Jekyll and Mr. Hyde*
3) Democratic presidential candidate assassinated in 1968
4) Atlanta Braves owner and founder of CNN who was named as *Time* magazine's 1991 "Man of the Year"
5) American who won the Pulitzer Prize for poetry in 1924, 1931, 1937, and 1943
6) Wisconsin senator represented in Statuary Hall in Washington, D.C.
7) American physician who designed the mechanical heart first implanted by surgeon DeVries in 1982
8) American who formed the American Ballet Center in 1954
9) Reagan nominee to the U.S. Supreme Court who was rejected by the Senate
10) Founder of the John Birch Society, in 1958

Answers:

1) Robert Boyle
2) Robert Louis Stevenson
3) Robert Kennedy
4) Robert Edward "Ted" Turner (III)
5) Robert Frost
6) Robert La Follette
7) Robert Jarvik
8) Robert Joffrey
9) Robert Bork
10) Robert Welch Jr.

RUSSIAN HISTORY

Identify each of the following concerning Russian history.

1) War that was an outgrowth of rivalry over control of Manchuria and Korea in 1904-1905
2) Czar who worked to westernize Russian from 1698-1725
3) Russian dynasty that ruled from 1613-1917
4) First czar of Russia, notorious for his cruelty and erratic behavior
5) Czar who was in power from 1825 to 1855
6) Grand prince of Kiev and first Christian ruler of Russia
7) Month for the revolution that led to the overthrow of the czar and the end of the 1613-1917 dynasty
8) Month for the revolution that brought the Bolsheviks to power in 1917
9) Legislative body that was created by Czar Nicholas II after the 1905 revolution
10) Czar who abolished serfdom in the U.S.S.R. in 1861

Answers:

1) Russo-Japanese War
2) Peter (I; or Peter the Great)
3) Romanov
4) Ivan (IV; or Ivan the Terrible)
5) Nicholas (I)
6) Vladimir (I; the Great or Saint Vladimir)
7) February Revolution
8) October Revolution (Russian Revolution)
9) Duma
10) Alexander (II)

DICKENS' CHARACTERS

Identify each of the following concerning characters created by Charles Dickens.

1) Man who dies instead of Charles Darnay in *A Tale of Two Cities*
2) Mean old man in *A Christmas Carol*
3) David Copperfield's great aunt
4) Sanctimonious hypocrite in *David Copperfield*
5) Hero of *Great Expectations*
6) "Doggedly optimistic person," a schemer in *David Copperfield*
7) Head of the pickpockets in *Oliver Twist*
8) The Artful Dodger
9) Knitting lady in *A Tale of Two Cities*
10) Overbearing beadle in *Oliver Twist*

Answers:

1) Sydney Carton
2) Ebenezer Scrooge
3) Betsey Trotwood
4) Uriah Heep
5) Pip (Philip Pirrip)
6) Mr. Wilkins Micawber
7) Fagin
8) Jack Dawkins
9) Mme. Defarge
10) Mr. Bumble

THE LETTER *A*

Identify each of the following by giving an answer beginning with the letter *A*.

1) U.S. President, nicknamed "Old Man Eloquent," whose father had signed the Declaration of Independence
2) Sin represented by the scarlet letter in a Nathaniel Hawthorne novel
3) Spanish word for an enthusiast or sports devotee
4) Person who does not believe in or denies the existence of a supreme being or beings
5) Simple organisms with chlorophyll that are the chief aquatic plant life
6) Black leader of American patriots, who was killed in the Boston Massacre
7) German word for "union" used to refer to the annexation of Austria by Hitler in 1938
8) Beautiful young man loved by Aphrodite and killed by a boar
9) Moorish citadel whose remains lie on a hill in Granada, Spain
10) Term indicating that a piece of music has no specific key

Answers:

1) (John Quincy) Adams
2) Adultery
3) Aficionado
4) Atheist (do NOT accept agnostic)
5) Algae
6) (Crispus) Attucks
7) Anschluss
8) Adonis
9) Alhambra
10) Atonality

HEART AND CIRCULATORY SYSTEM

Identify each of the following concerning the human heart and circulatory system.

1) Large blood vessel that receives blood from the heart's left ventricle and sends it to the rest of the body
2) Blood vessels that carry blood from the body tissues back to the heart
3) High blood pressure
4) Deposits of fat, cholesterol, and other substances that line blood vessels
5) Outer membrane that surrounds the heart
6) Blood vessels that carry blood from the heart to the body
7) Sac formed by an enlargement of a weakened blood vessel, caused by disease or injury
8) Study of heart functions and its diseases
9) Adjective used to describe any heart defect present at birth
10) Thickening of the walls of blood vessels, sometimes called hardening of the arteries

Answers:

1) Aorta
2) Veins
3) Hypertension
4) Plaque
5) Pericardium
6) Arteries (accept arterioles or capillaries)
7) Aneurysm
8) Cardiology
9) Congenital
10) Arteriosclerosis (accept atherosclerosis)

POTPOURRI OF HISTORICAL HIGHLIGHTS

Identify each of the following potpourri of historical highlights.

1) Scottish poem by Robert Burns sung on New Year's Eve to mark the passing of another year
2) U.S. state where the Winter Olympic Games were held in Squaw Valley in 1960
3) U.S. President who initiated the Peace Corps
4) South American liberator after whom Bolivia was named
5) American ornithologist, born in Haiti, who published his first volume of *The Birds of America* in 1827
6) More common name for a machine called a polygraph
7) Space vehicle launched by the Soviets in 1957 whose name means "traveling companion"
8) U.S. President who is the subject of Piers Brendon's biography *Ike: His Life & Times*
9) American Indian whose husband was John Rolfe
10) Patriotic song which begins, "O beautiful for spacious skies, / For amber waves of grain"

Answers:

1) "Auld Lang Syne"
2) California
3) John F. Kennedy
4) Simón Bolívar
5) John James Audubon
6) Lie detector
7) Sputnik
8) Dwight Eisenhower
9) Pocahontas (accept Matoaka or Rebecca)
10) "America the Beautiful"

HORNS

Identify each of the following concerning *horns*.

1) Mythical animal, similar to a horse, with a single horn projecting from its forehead
2) Continent on which Cape Horn is located
3) Country located on the "Horn of Africa"
4) Southwest Conference team known as the "Longhorns"
5) Site where Custer made his last stand
6) Countries on whose borders the Matterhorn is located
7) Animal whose name means "nose horn"
8) Latin word for "horn of plenty"
9) 10th sign of the Zodiac, the Horned Goat with the tail of a fish
10) Knight urged to sound his horn in the 11th century anonymous French poem that bears his name: "*Chanson de* ______"

Answers:

1) Unicorn
2) South America
3) Somalia
4) University of Texas
5) Little Big Horn
6) Switzerland and Italy
7) Rhinoceros
8) Cornucopia
9) Capricornus (accept Capricorn)
10) Roland

THE WORD *TIME*

Identify each of the following associated with the word *time*.

1) U.S. presidential candidate who said, "These unhappy times call for . . . plans . . . that put their faith . . . in . . . the forgotten man at the bottom of the economic pyramid."
2) "King of the Ragtime Composers"
3) English author of *Hard Times*
4) American author of *My Life and Hard Times*
5) Word designating a time inaccuracy such as the mention of a striking clock in Shakespeare's *Julius Caesar*
6) Term for time required for half the atoms of a radioactive substance to decay into another substance
7) Leader who said, "For the second time in our history, a British Prime Minister has returned from Germany bringing peace with honor."
8) Cambridge physicist and mathematician who wrote *A Brief History of Time*
9) French author of *Remembrance of Things Past*, an introspective journey "in search of lost time"
10) English poet who wrote, "Gather ye rosebuds while ye may, / Old Time is still a-flying"

Answers:

1) Franklin Roosevelt
2) Scott Joplin
3) Charles Dickens
4) James Thurber
5) Anachronism
6) Half-life (accept radioactive half-life or half-value period)
7) Neville Chamberlain
8) Stephen William Hawking
9) Marcel Proust
10) Robert Herrick (from "To the Virgins to Make Much of Time")

A *BEAR*ABLE CATEGORY

Identify each of the following associated with the word *bear*.

1) U.S. President who refused to shoot a black bear cub and after whom stuffed animals called "teddy bears" were named
2) Country in which Great Bear Lake is located
3) Latin name for the constellation known as the Great Bear or Big Bear
4) Bears with a hump on their shoulders that distinguishes them from other bears
5) American author who wrote the story "The Bear"
6) U.S. state known as "The Bear Flag Republic" and on whose flag is a bear
7) Fictional bear who lives in Jellystone Park
8) Fictional bear living in Alaska in a story by Walter Morey
9) Largest living meat-eating land animal
10) Pro golfer known as "The Bear" or "The Golden Bear"

Answers:

1) Theodore Roosevelt
2) Canada
3) Ursa Major
4) Grizzly bears (accept brown bear)
5) William Faulkner
6) California
7) Yogi Bear (accept Booboo Bear)
8) Gentle Ben
9) Alaskan brown bear (accept Kodiak bear)
10) Jack Nicklaus

FAMOUS PEOPLE WITH THE SAME SURNAMES

Identify the surname shared by all three famous people in the following groups.

1) Shoeless Joe, Bo, Mahalia
2) Sir John, Benjamin, Aretha
3) Henry, John, Edsel
4) John Napier, J.M.W., Nat
5) Casey, Davy, Mary Harris
6) Walter, Samuel, James Weldon
7) Glenn, Gerald, Ford Madox
8) William, Jesse, P.D.
9) Ethel, John, Lionel
10) Richard, Ethan, Woody

Answers:

1) Jackson
2) Franklin
3) Ford
4) Turner
5) Jones
6) Johnson
7) Ford
8) James
9) Barrymore
10) Allen

THE LETTER *B*

Identify each of the following by giving an answer beginning with the letter *B*.

1) German word for lightning warfare or a sudden military offensive by air and ground forces
2) First Jewish Justice on the U.S. Supreme Court
3) Literary work featuring Hrothgar and Grendel
4) U.S. President who immediately preceded Lincoln in office
5) U.S. capital city where Huey Long was fatally shot in 1935
6) Sanskrit term for "the enlightened one"
7) French composer of the opera *Carmen*
8) American called the "First Black Man of Science" and "The African Astronomer"
9) Base whose formula is $Ba(OH)_2$
10) Confederate general who said, "There is Jackson, standing like a stone wall!"

Answers:

1) Blitzkrieg
2) (Louis) Brandeis
3) *Beowulf*
4) (James) Buchanan
5) Baton Rouge
6) Buddha
7) (Georges) Bizet
8) (Benjamin) Banneker
9) Barium hydroxide
10) (Bernard Elliott) Bee

FAMOUS IN THE FIELD OF CHEMISTRY

Identify each of the following famous people in the field of chemistry.

1) Italian physicist who suggested that equal volumes of all gases at the same temperature and pressure contain equal numbers of molecules
2) English chemist who independently discovered oxygen
3) French chemist whose oxygen theory of combustion replaced the phlogiston theory
4) English "Founder of Experimental Science"
5) English chemist and physicist who identified hydrogen as an element and showed that water is a compound of oxygen and hydrogen
6) Irish scientist who showed that earth, air, fire, and water are not true elements
7) English physicist who discovered a mathematical relationship between electricity and the valence of a chemical element
8) English chemist who developed an atomic theory that each chemical element has its own kinds of atoms
9) Greek philosopher who introduced the idea that all matter is composed of tiny, indestructible units called atoms
10) Greek philosopher who believed that there were 4 elements: earth, air, fire, and water

Answers:

1) Amedeo Avogadro
2) Joseph Priestley
3) Antoine Lavoisier
4) Roger Bacon
5) Henry Cavendish
6) Robert Boyle
7) Michael Faraday
8) John Dalton
9) Democritus
10) Empedocles

MEASURES

Identify each of the following concerning measures.

1) Number of cubic feet in a cubic yard times 2
2) Number of cups in a pint times 43
3) 6 dozen times 3
4) Number of feet in a yard times 41
5) Number of square inches in a square foot times 3
6) Baker's dozen times 4
7) Number of quarts in a gallon times 16
8) Gross times 2
9) Number of teaspoons in a tablespoon times 10
10) Number of ounces in a pint times 9

Answers:

1) 54
2) 86
3) 216
4) 123
5) 432
6) 52
7) 64
8) 288
9) 30
10) 144

AMERICAN CREATORS OF LITERARY CHARACTERS

Identify the American author who created each of the following characters.

1) Amanda Wingfield
2) Biff Loman
3) Aunt Polly
4) Madeline Usher
5) Philip Nolan
6) Tom Joad
7) Phineas
8) George and Emily Webb (Emily Gibbs before the marriage)
9) Miss Pyncheon
10) Santiago

Answers:

1) Tennessee Williams
2) Arthur Miller
3) Mark Twain (accept Samuel Clemens)
4) Edgar Allan Poe
5) Edward Hale
6) John Steinbeck
7) John Knowles
8) Thornton Wilder
9) Nathaniel Hawthorne
10) Ernest Hemingway

AMERICAN WOMEN IN POLITICS

Identify each of the following women in U.S. politics.

1) First woman to serve on U.S. Supreme Court, a Reagan-appointee in 1981
2) First woman to be major party's U.S. vice presidential nominee, in 1984
3) First black woman in Congress, elected in Brooklyn, New York, in 1968
4) First black Congressperson from Deep South since 1900, elected in 1972
5) First woman to serve in the U.S. Senate, a Georgia appointee in 1922
6) Montana woman elected U.S.'s first Congresswoman, in 1916
7) First woman to serve as mayor of Chicago, from 1979 to 1983
8) Second woman to serve on the U.S. Supreme Court, starting in 1993
9) First woman elected governor, succeeding her husband in Wyoming in 1925
10) Laborite who led both men and women in United Mine Worker strikes in early 20th century

Answers:

1) Sandra D. O'Connor
2) Geraldine Ferraro
3) Shirley Chisholm
4) Barbara Jordan
5) Rebecca Felton
6) Jeannette Rankin
7) Jane Byrne
8) Ruth Ginsburg
9) Nellie Tayloe Ross
10) Mother Jones (or Mary Harris Jones)

TOM, DICK, AND HARRY

Identify each of the following by giving an answer with Tom, Dick, or Harry.

1) Author of *Patriot Games*, *The Hunt for Red October*, and *Red Storm Rising*
2) Comic strip character created by Chester Gould in 1931
3) U.S. President known for the motto, "The buck stops here"
4) Los Angeles mayor who won a fifth consecutive term in 1989
5) Completion of the Washington Irving's story *The Devil and* __________
6) Novel featuring Ishmael and the *Pequod*
7) Magician born Ehrich Weiss in Hungary in 1874
8) *Grapes of Wrath* character who carries on Jim Casy's work
9) Author of *The Bonfire of the Vanities*
10) Legendary English highwayman known as "The King of the Road" because of his daring deeds

Answers:

1) Tom Clancy
2) Dick Tracy
3) Harry S Truman
4) Tom Bradley
5) *Tom Walker*
6) *Moby Dick*
7) Harry Houdini
8) Tom Joad
9) Tom Wolfe
10) Dick Turpin

REAGAN AND HIS ADMINISTRATION

Identify each of the following concerning President Ronald Reagan and his administration(s).

1) His wife while President
2) His first wife
3) First Secretary of State
4) 2nd Secretary of State
5) First Secretary of Defense
6) Assassin who wounded him in 1981
7) Presidential Secretary wounded in this assassination attempt
8) 1986 public scandal concerning sales of weapons and aid for the Nicaraguan rebels
9) First Secretary of Treasury
10) First secretary of the Interior

Answers:

1) Nancy (Davis)
2) Jane Wyman
3) Alexander Haig
4) George Schultz
5) Casper Weinberger
6) John Hinckley
7) James Brady
8) Iran-*contra*
9) Donald Regan
10) James Watt

THE LETTER *C*

Identify each of the following by giving an answer beginning with the letter *C*.

1) 1854-1856 war fought between Russia and the allied powers of Turkey, Britain, France, and Sardinia
2) Art picture that exaggerates the physical features of a person
3) Three-headed dog of the underworld in Greek myth
4) Founder of Detroit, in 1701
5) U.S. President who said, "If you don't say anything, you won't be called on to repeat it."
6) Nickname of John Kennedy's administration derived from Arthurian legend
7) Person in Greek history whose name is synonymous with a very rich person
8) Acid whose formula is $HClO_3$
9) King of Denmark, Hamlet's uncle
10) Latin name for the constellation The Lady in the Chair

Answers:

1) Crimean War
2) Caricature
3) Cerberus
4) (Antoine de la Mothe) Cadillac
5) (Calvin) Coolidge
6) Camelot
7) Croesus
8) Chloric acid
9) Claudius
10) Cassiopeia

CHEMICAL ELEMENTS

Identify each of the following concerning chemical elements.

1) 4th most common element in the earth's crust, the one that forms ferrous and ferric compounds
2) Term for elements fluorine, chlorine, bromine, iodine, and astatine
3) German name for the element tungsten
4) Number of neutrons in an atom of an element whose atomic number is 6 and mass number is 14
5) Term for number of protons in the nucleus of an atom of a chemical element
6) Second most abundant element in the earth's crust (about 28% by weight)
7) Only radioactive element that occurs naturally as a gas
8) Element named after one of a family of giants in Greek mythology
9) Yellow nonmetallic element, equated with the Biblical brimstone
10) British chemist who prepared the first periodic table of the elements arranged in the order of atomic weights

Answers:

1) Iron
2) Halogens
3) Wolfram
4) 8
5) Atomic number
6) Silicon
7) Radon
8) Titanium
9) Sulfur (or sulphur)
10) John Alexander Newlands

MATH TERMS

Identify each of the following terms used in math.

1) Mathematical property stating that x times the sum of y and $z = xy + xz$ (equals x times y plus x times z)
2) Polynomial consisting of three terms
3) Divisor of an integer
4) One of the two congruent sides of an isosceles triangle
5) Portion of a sphere sliced off by a plane passing through the sphere's center
6) Word used to designate 2 geometric figures having the same shape and the same size
7) Specific example that shows that a general statement is false
8) In calculus, the limit of one over x^2 as x approaches 0 (zero)
9) Synonym for *the null set*
10) In geometry, line segment whose length is the height of a polygon or a polyhedron

Answers:

1) Distribution (property; accept distributive)
2) Trinomial
3) Factor
4) Leg
5) Hemisphere
6) Congruent
7) Counterexample
8) Infinity (accept infinite)
9) Empty set
10) Altitude

BRITISH WORKS

Name the British author of each of the following literary works.

1) *Vanity Fair, or a Novel Without a Hero*
2) *Lord of the Flies*
3) *Brideshead Revisited*
4) *Great Expectations*
5) *She Stoops to Conquer*
6) *Animal Farm*
7) *Pilgrim's Progress*
8) *Gulliver's Travels*
9) *Silas Marner*
10) *Prometheus Unbound*

Answers:

1) William Makepeace Thackeray
2) William Golding
3) Evelyn Waugh
4) Charles Dickens
5) Oliver Goldsmith
6) George Orwell
7) John Bunyan
8) Jonathan Swift
9) George Eliot
10) Percy Bysshe Shelley

SOCIOLOGY

Identify these terms taken from the field of sociology.

1) Actions following current norm
2) An official count of population
3) French word for the middle class
4) Name for social classes in Hindu India
5) Attribution of human feelings to the non-human
6) Leaving one country to settle in another
7) Belief that one's race or ethnic group is superior
8) Community or society with power concentrated in females
9) The working class
10) Emotional isolation or estrangement

Answer:

1) Conformity
2) Census
3) Bourgeoisie
4) Castes
5) Anthropomorphism
6) Emigration
7) Ethnocentrism (accept racism)
8) Matriarchy
9) Proletariat
10) Alienation

ARCHAEOLOGY

Identify each of the following concerning archaeology.

1) Erect, Caucasoid distinguished by his erect stature whose remains were found in a cave in France in 1868
2) Technique using an isotope to discover age of fossils
3) Period before written records
4) Genus and species of modern humans
5) Term designating the process of carefully digging for buried objects
6) Extinct human species found in China
7) Extinct human species found in East Africa
8) New Stone Age
9) Old Stone Age
10) Extinct early human found in Germany

Answer:

1) Cro-Magnon Man
2) Carbon 14 Dating
3) Prehistory
4) Homo sapiens (sapiens)
5) Excavation
6) Peking Man
7) Homo habilis
8) Neolithic
9) Paleolithic
10) Heidelberg or Neanderthal Man

MAIN CHARACTERS IN AMERICAN NOVELS

Give the title of the work in which the following characters appear.

1) Newland Archer; May Welland; Ellen Olenska
2) Uncle Tom; Eva St. Clare; Simon Legree
3) McMurphy; Miss Ratched; Chief Bromden
4) Holden Caulfield; Phoebe Caulfield
5) Henry Fleming; Jim Conklin; Wilson
6) Yossarian; Milo Minderbinder; Major
7) Celie; Shug Avery; Sophia Butler
8) Lennie Small; George Milton; Candy; Curley
9) Billy Pilgrim; Benard V. O'Hare; Montana Wildhack
10) Bigger Thomas; Mary Dalton; Bessie Mears; Jan Erlone

Answers:

1) *Age of Innocence*
2) *Uncle Tom's Cabin*
3) *One Flew Over the Cuckoo's Nest*
4) *The Catcher in the Rye*
5) *The Red Badge of Courage*
6) *Catch-22*
7) *The Color Purple*
8) *Of Mice and Men*
9) *Slaughterhouse Five*
10) *Native Son*

THE LETTER *D*

Identify each of the following by giving an answer beginning with the letter *D*.

1) Congenital syndrome characterized by chromosome abnormality, severe mental retardation, a short skull, and slanting eyes
2) Englishman who circumnavigated the world on the *Golden Hind*
3) Country on Jutland Peninsula
4) Avian symbol of peace
5) Skin specialist
6) Stringed musical instrument in a shallow closed box known for its soft, sweet sound
7) Change in the structure of an atomic nucleus by its emissions of particles or radiation
8) Second longest river in Europe
9) Unknown person who is nominated for or wins a political race
10) French composer of *Prelude to the Afternoon of a Faun*

Answers:

1) Down's syndrome (Down syndrome)
2) (Sir Francis) Drake
3) Denmark
4) Dove
5) Dermatologist
6) Dulcimer (or dulcimore)
7) Disintegration (accept decay)
8) Danube River
9) Dark horse
10) (Claude) Debussy

SCIENCE

Identify each of the following concerning science.

1) Vitamin into which animals can convert carotene, the red or yellow crystalline pigment found in the carrot
2) Term that designates the part of the skull that encloses the brain
3) Largest artery in the human body
4) Mass of a paperclip in the SI system
5) Planet that has been the farthest from the sun since 1979 and will remain so until 1999
6) Disease-causing microbe whose name is derived from the Latin word for "poison"
7) Word ending in *-sphere* that designates the layer of the atmosphere closest to the earth
8) Gas that makes up 21% of the earth's atmosphere, second to nitrogen at about 78%
9) Insects of the order Isoptera that are often pests of agricultural crops and wooden buildings
10) More common name for the part of the human hand known as the carpus

Answers:

1) Vitamin A
2) Cranium (accept braincase)
3) Aorta
4) One gram
5) Neptune
6) Virus
7) Troposphere
8) Oxygen
9) Termites (do NOT accept white ants)
10) Wrist

COMPLETION OF FAMOUS TRIPLETS

Identify the 3rd for each of the following famous triplets.

1) Igneous, metamorphic, _________
2) Bach, Beethoven, _________
3) Abraham, Isaac, _________
4) Wynken, Blynken, _________
5) Protons, neutrons, _________
6) Faith, Hope, _________
7) Charlotte, Anne, _________
8) Foil, épée, _________
9) Regan, Goneril, _________
10) Athos, Porthos, _________

Answers:

1) sedimentary
2) Brahms
3) Jacob
4) Nod
5) electrons
6) Charity (accept love)
7) Emily
8) saber
9) Cordelia
10) Aramis

AMERICAN POETS AND THEIR POEMS

Identify the poet who wrote each of the following.

1) "Stopping by Woods on a Snowy Evening"
2) "Because I could not stop for Death"
3) "Song of Myself"
4) "The Courtship of Miles Standish"
5) "I Hear America Singing"
6) "Ichabod"
7) "Annabel Lee"
8) "The Deacon's Masterpiece" (or "The Wonderful One-Hoss Shay")
9) "The Rhodora"
10) "To a Waterfowl"

Answers:

1) Robert Frost
2) Emily Dickinson
3) Walt Whitman
4) Henry Wadsworth Longfellow
5) Walt Whitman
6) John Greenleaf Whittier
7) Edgar Allan Poe
8) Oliver Wendell Holmes
9) Ralph Waldo Emerson
10) William Cullen Bryant

POTPOURRI

Identify each of the following.

1) U.S. capital city where a famous 375-member choir performs in the Mormon Tabernacle in Temple Square
2) Letter of the Greek alphabet that begins with *I* and means "a very small quantity"
3) American showman to whom is attributed the line, "There's a sucker born every minute"
4) Number of "winks" in the expression for "a brief nap" or "a short period of relaxation"
5) Breed of retrievers named after part of a large peninsula in north-eastern Canada
6) Space shuttle aboard which 7 U.S. astronauts died in 1986
7) Major U.S. corporation nicknamed "Big Blue"
8) Former U.S. federal prison named from the Spanish for "pelican" and located in San Francisco
9) Word for a 500th anniversary
10) Author remembered for cabling from London, "The reports of my death are greatly exaggerated"

Answers:

1) Salt Lake City (Utah)
2) Iota
3) P.T. Barnum
4) 40
5) Labrador
6) *Challenger*
7) IBM (or International Business Machines)
8) Alcatraz
9) Quincentennial
10) Mark Twain (or Samuel Langhorne Clemens)

COMPLETION OF OPERA TITLES

Complete the title of each of the following operas.

1) *The Marriage of* _________
2) *The Magic* _________
3) *William* _________
4) *The Threepenny* _________
5) *The Barber of* _________
6) *Boris* _________
7) *La Fanciulla del* _________
8) *Cavalleria* _________
9) *Lucia Di* _________
10) *Eugene* _________

Answers:

1) *Figaro*
2) *Flute*
3) *Tell*
4) *Opera*
5) *Seville*
6) *Godunov*
7) *West*
8) *Rusticana*
9) *Lammermoor*
10) *Onegin*

ANSWERS WITH DOUBLE LETTERS

Identify each of the following with an answer that includes a doubling of the given letter.

1) F - Shakespearean character who says, "I am not only witty in myself, but the cause that wit is in other men"
2) B - Group of people who attempt to influence public officials
3) C - Roman name for the god of wine
4) D - Current of water moving against a main current, especially when having a whirling motion
5) E - Part of the body known as the patella
6) A - First name of the man who killed Alexander Hamilton in a duel
7) G - New York city museum designed by Frank Lloyd Wright
8) I - Pacific Ocean islands on which Captain James Cook was killed in 1779
9) L - British poet who wrote "To a Skylark" and the elegy *Adonais*
10) K - One of the 4 major civilizations of ancient Mesopotamia that fits this category

Answers:

1) Falstaff
2) Lobby (accept lobbyists)
3) Bacchus
4) Eddy
5) Kneecap
6) Aaron (Burr)
7) Guggenheim Museum
8) Hawaiian Islands (Hawaii)
9) (Percy Bysshe) Shelley
10) Akkadian

THE LETTER *E*

Identify each of the following by giving an answer beginning with the letter *E*.

1) German-American scientist who said, "The unleashed power of the atom has changed everything save our modes of thinking."
2) Organ system of the human body that regulates various body functions through internal secretions
3) Country whose name means "equator"
4) Greek author of *Medea*
5) Order of the organism known as mayflies
6) Viking who colonized Greenland about A.D. 985
7) Greek god of love
8) Castle that is the setting for Shakespeare's *Hamlet*
9) Term for the body's internal skeleton
10) African country whose name is derived from the Greek for "people with sunburnt faces"

Answers:

1) (Albert) Einstein
2) Endocrine
3) Ecuador
4) Euripides
5) Ephemeroptera
6) Eric the Red (Eric Thorvaldson or Erik Thorvaldsson)
7) Eros
8) Elsinore Castle
9) Endoskeleton
10) Ethiopia

DIGESTIVE SYSTEM

Identify each of the following concerning the digestive system.

1) Of the 3 main classes of nutrients, the one that provides the main source of energy to the body
2) Waxy, fatty substance produced by the liver
3) Fingerlike projections lining the small intestine
4) Muscle that opens and closes a body opening, such as the rectum
5) Term for the "building blocks of proteins"
6) Process by which cells convert food into living tissue after digestion
7) Duct into which bile flows from liver before connecting with the common bile duct
8) Small, pear-shaped pouch attached to the common bile duct
9) Wavelike contractions that push food through the alimentary canal
10) Food tube leading from the pharynx to the stomach

Answers:

1) Carbohydrate
2) Cholesterol
3) Villi
4) Sphincter
5) Amino acids
6) Assimilation (accept anabolism)
7) Hepatic duct
8) Gall bladder
9) Peristalsis
10) Esophagus

MATH TERMS

Identify each of the following terms used in math.

1) 4-letter adjective that describes 2 lines that are neither parallel nor intersecting
2) In geometry, name given to a statement accepted as true without proof
3) Line segment joining any 2 points on a circle
4) Type of logarithm that uses the number *e* as its base
5) Two angles whose measures have a sum of 180 degrees
6) Statement that can be proved easily by applying a theorem
7) Point of concurrency of the altitudes of a triangle
8) In solid geometry, the set consisting of all points at a given distance from a fixed point
9) Segment drawn from a vertex of a triangle to the midpoint of the opposite side
10) Coordinate system in which coordinates of points are in the form (*r*, theta)

Answers:

1) Skew
2) Postulate (accept axiom)
3) Chord (do NOT accept diameter)
4) Natural (accept Napierian)
5) Supplementary angles
6) Corollary
7) Orthocenter
8) Sphere
9) Median
10) Polar

THE WORD *PRINCE*

Identify the following, each of which is associated with the word *prince*.

1) Fairy tale heroine who is maltreated by a spiteful stepmother but marries a prince
2) Trojan prince whose name today means "to bully" or "to intimidate"
3) Crown Prince who succeeded his father, Emperor Hirohito, in 1989
4) German-born Consort of Queen Victoria
5) Professional sports league with a Prince of Wales Conference
6) Tchaikovsky ballet that includes the wicked fairy, Prince Florimund, and Princess Aurora
7) Title given to the first male heir to the throne of Great Britain
8) Husband of Queen Elizabeth II
9) Novel featuring Prince Rupert of Ruritania
10) Austrian chancellor with the title of prince who was the guiding spirit of the 1814-1815 Congress of Vienna

Answers:

1) Cinderella
2) Hector
3) Akihito
4) Prince Albert
5) National Hockey League
6) *Sleeping Beauty*
7) Prince of Wales
8) Prince Philip (Mountbatten)
9) *The Prisoner of Zenda* (accept *Rupert of Hentzau*)
10) Prince (Klemens) von Metternich (accept Metternich)

FAMOUS PEOPLE WITH THE SAME SURNAMES

Identify the surname shared by all three famous people in the following groups.

1) George, John, Thurgood
2) Charles William, George, T.S.
3) Prescott, George, Barbara
4) George, Marianne, Clement Clarke
5) Byron "Whizzer," T.H., E.B.
6) Richard, Wilbur, Frank Lloyd
7) Billy, Thornton, Laura Ingalls
8) John, Margaret, "Billy"
9) Thomas Henry, Sir Julian Sorell, Aldous
10) Henry, Glenn, Arthur

Answers:

1) Marshall
2) Eliot
3) Bush
4) Moore
5) White
6) Wright
7) Wilder
8) Mitchell
9) Huxley
10) Miller

THE WORD *BELL*

Identify each of the following associated with the word *bell*.

1) U.S. Supreme Court Chief Justice for whose death the Liberty Bell was tolling on July 8, 1835, when it cracked
2) American author of *For Whom the Bell Tolls*
3) Scientist who reportedly made experiments at the Leaning Tower of Pisa, a famous bell tower
4) American artist known for his depiction of Camp*bell*'s Soup cans
5) City in which the Liberty Bell is located
6) Oil company targeted by Ida Tar*bell*'s 1904 exposé of the practices of some great corporations
7) Former U.S. President who in 1820 described the Missouri Compromise as "a firebell in the night"
8) English novelist who used the pseudonym Currer Bell
9) American author of *A Bell for Adano*
10) Biblical source for the Liberty Bell's inscription, "Proclaim liberty throughout all the land unto all the inhabitants thereof"

Answers:

1) John Marshall
2) Ernest Hemingway
3) Galileo
4) Andy Warhol
5) Philadelphia
6) Standard Oil
7) Thomas Jefferson
8) Charlotte Brontë
9) John Hersey
10) Leviticus (25:10)

PYRAMIDS

Identify each of the following concerning pyramids.

1) Temple of Sumerian origin in the form of a pyramidal tower with each story smaller than the one below it
2) Name of the "Great Pyramid," the largest ever built
3) Another name for a triangular pyramid or a polyhedron with 4 faces
4) Chinese-American architect who designed the Louvre's glass pyramid
5) Tennessee city where a $65-million pyramid on the bank of the Wolf River is located
6) Egyptian architect of the first known pyramid, the *Step Pyramid* near Saqqarah built for King Zoser
7) Egyptian suburb of Cairo where the largest pyramid ever built exists
8) Formula for the volume of a regular pyramid
9) Latin American country in which The Pyramid of the Sun was built at Teotihuacán
10) South American country in which the Mochica Indians built The Pyramid of the Sun near Trujillo

Answers:

1) Ziggurat (also zikkurat or zikurat)
2) Pyramid of Khufu or Cheops
3) Tetrahedron
4) I.M. Pei
5) Memphis
6) Imhotep
7) Giza
8) $V = Bh$ over 3, in which B is the area of the base and h the height (or one-third the area of the base times the height).
9) Mexico
10) Peru (called the *Huaca del Sol*)

THE LETTER *F*

Identify each of the following by giving an answer beginning with the letter *F*.

1) Ironic name of victim whom Montressor buries alive in Poe's "The Cask of Amontillado"
2) French phrase for a woman who lures her lovers to disaster
3) Legendary ghost ship doomed to sail eternally
4) Jewish U.S. Supreme Court justice who served from 1939-1962
5) Alaska's second largest city, one nicknamed the "Golden Heart of the North"
6) Inventor of the *Clermont*, the first commercially successful steamboat
7) Stalklike part of a stamen that supports the anther in flowers
8) Inventor of the first practical mercury thermometer
9) Author of *The Hamlet*, *The Mansion*, and *The Reivers*
10) Scientist who demonstrated the rotation of the Earth with his pendulum

Answers:

1) Fortunato
2) Femme fatale
3) *Flying Dutchman*
4) (Felix) Frankfurter
5) Fairbanks
6) (Robert) Fulton
7) Filament
8) (Gabriel Daniel) Fahrenheit
9) (William) Faulkner
10) (Jean Bernard) Foucault

SCIENCE

Identify each of the following.

1) Three-letter abbreviation of adenosine triphosphate, a phosphorus compound that supplies organisms with energy
2) Either of 2 organs that supplies the blood with oxygen and removes carbon dioxide from it
3) Two main elements in table salt
4) Planet Sir William Herschel discovered on March 13, 1781
5) More common name for the Sequoia sempervirens, the world's tallest living tree
6) Uncharged elementary particle in the nucleus of an atom
7) Planet and element named for a god known for his speed
8) Group of chemical elements made up of "salt producers"
9) Vitamin also called ascorbic acid
10) Flexible tissue that gives support and shape to body parts and is not bone

Answers:

1) ATP
2) Lung
3) Sodium and chlorine
4) Uranus
5) Redwood (accept California redwood or coastal redwood)
6) Neutron
7) Mercury
8) Halogens
9) Vitamin C
10) Cartilage (accept gristle)

QUICK MATH

Answer each of the following quick math questions.

1) How many more edges than vertices does a cube have?
2) What is the length in feet of one edge of a cube with volume 27 cubic feet?
3) What is the multiplicative inverse of 6?
4) Which of the following is always a parallelogram: trapezoid, polygon, triangle, rectangle, or quadrilateral?
5) What is 300% of 800?
6) What irrational number is used as the base for natural logarithms?
7) What is 1/2 of 1/2 of 1/2?
8) If the radius of a sphere is doubled, by what factor is its volume multiplied?
9) What is the equivalent degree measure of an angle that is *pi* radians?
10) If a prism has a quadrilateral for a base, how many lateral faces does it have?

Answers:

1) 4 (12 – 8)
2) 3 (feet)
3) One-sixth
4) Rectangle
5) 2,400
6) *e* (do not accept 2.718 or any other approximation of *e*)
7) 1/8 (accept .125)
8) 8
9) 180
10) 4

ANSWERS WITH DOUBLE LETTERS

Identify each of the following with an answer that includes a doubling of the given letter.

1) P - Name of the figure formed by 7 bright stars in the constellation Ursa Minor, or Little Bear
2) M - Electromagnetic rays like X rays, but with a shorter wavelength
3) E - 17th century American poetess known as the "Tenth Muse"
4) T - Leaf-shaped structure that acts like a lid to prevent swallowed food from entering the windpipe
5) L - Civil War battle also known as Manassas
6) R - British author who created the Cheshire Cat and the Mad Hatter
7) S - Jewish festival that celebrates the flight of the Israelites from Egyptian slavery
8) O - Components of an ordered pair giving the location of a point in the Cartesian plane
9) N - 1940 Harvard graduate whose senior thesis was *Why England Slept*
10) Z - Capital of the Congo

Answers:

1) Little Dipper
2) Gamma (rays)
3) (Anne) Bradstreet
4) Epiglottis
5) Bull Run
6) (Lewis) Carroll
7) Passover
8) Coordinates (accept coordinate)
9) (John) Kennedy
10) Brazzaville

IDENTIFY THE YEAR

Identify the year for each of the following.

1) Ruth hit 60 homers and Lindbergh flew the Atlantic
2) Martin Luther King and Bobby Kennedy were killed
3) Federal Reserve was created and Wilson served his first year in office
4) Pony Express began and Lincoln was elected
5) Alaska was purchased and Britain made Canada a dominion
6) Hamilton was killed by Burr and Napoleon crowned himself emperor
7) 20th Amendment was ratified and FDR was inaugurated
8) *Titanic* sank and Arizona and New Mexico joined the Union
9) Atlantic Charter was proclaimed and Japan attacked Pearl Harbor
10) NATO treaty was ratified and Berlin blockade was lifted

Answers:

1) 1927
2) 1968
3) 1913
4) 1860
5) 1867
6) 1804
7) 1933
8) 1912
9) 1941
10) 1949

LATIN ABBREVIATIONS

Give the Latin for each of the following abbreviations.

1) m.o.
2) A.M.
3) c., ca.
4) A.D.
5) e.g.
6) et. al.
7) etc.
8) ibid.
9) i.e.
10) cf.

Answers:

1) *modus operandi*
2) *ante meridiem*
3) *circa*
4) *anno domini*
5) *exempli gratia*
6) *et alii* (accept *et aliae* and *et alia*; accept *et alibi*, meaning "and elsewhere")
7) *et cetera*
8) *ibidem*
9) *id est*
10) *confer*

SPANISH PHRASES

Give the English for each of the following Spanish phrases.

1) *¿qué tal?*
2) *otra vez*
3) *más tarde*
4) *todo el mundo*
5) *poco a poco*
6) *a tiempo*
7) *de nada*
8) *esta noche*
9) *un poco de*
10) *a menudo*

Answers:

1) How are things?
2) Again
3) Later
4) Everyone
5) Gradually (accept little by little)
6) On time
7) You're welcome
8) Tonight
9) A little bit of
10) Often

THE LETTER *G*

Identify each of the following by giving an answer beginning with the letter *G*.

1) Abolitionist who wrote, "I am in earnest—I will not equivocate . . . I will not retreat a single inch—AND I WILL BE HEARD."
2) Specialist in the treatment of disease in women
3) French artist on whose life Somerset Maugham's *The Moon and Sixpence* is based
4) Knight who beheads the *Green* Knight in a medieval romance
5) Novel with Frank Kennedy, Charles Hamilton, and Bonnie Blue Butler
6) Architectural style known for its pointed arches and flying buttresses
7) Disease characterized by an enlarged thyroid gland, or goiter
8) West African country surrounded by Senegal
9) American general who defeated the British at Saratoga
10) State in which all the electrons in an atom are in the lowest energy levels available

Answers:

1) (William Lloyd) Garrison
2) Gynecologist
3) (Paul) Gauguin
4) (Sir) Gawain
5) *Gone With the Wind* (by Margaret Mitchell)
6) Gothic
7) Graves' disease
8) Gambia
9) (Horatio) Gates
10) Ground state

SCIENCE

Identify each of the following.

1) More common name for hydrophobia, a disease named from its victims' symptomatic inability to swallow water
2) Family of gaseous elements constituting Group VIII or Group O of the periodic table
3) Chemical element that exists in nature as diamonds and graphite
4) Name given to the force that causes an object going around in a circle to move away from the center
5) Name given to any plant that lacks chlorophyll and lives by feeding off other plants, or animals, alive or dead
6) Term beginning with the letter *D* used to designate teeth that fall out early in life several years after erupting
7) Class of rock formed by the cooling and hardening of molten matter brought from inside the earth to its surface
8) Layer of tissue at the back of the eye that transmits an image along the optic nerve to the brain
9) Number of atoms found in a molecule of ozone
10) Class of rock formed when particles of mineral and other matter are deposited on the bottom of a river or lake

Answers:

1) Rabies
2) Inert, or noble, gases (accept rare gases and helium group gases)
3) Carbon
4) Centrifugal force
5) Fungus (accept fungi, the plural form; accept saprophyte)
6) Deciduous (teeth)
7) Igneous rock
8) Retina
9) 3
10) Sedimentary rock

QUICK MATH

Identify each of the following.

1) Number of the quadrant in the Cartesian coordinate system in which the ordered pair (–2,–3) lies (READ: negative two, negative three)
2) Plane region bounded by two radii (ra-de-eye) and an arc of a circle
3) Two cubed times three squared
4) Plane region bounded by an arc of a circle and the chord of that arc
5) Decimal equivalent of 3/8
6) Amplitude of the sine function
7) Name of the conic section with equation $y - x^2 = 1$
8) One of the two imaginary square roots of negative 4
9) Dimensions of a matrix which is the sum of 2 square matrices of order 2
10) Value of the golden ratio when rounded to the nearest integer

Answers:

1) 3
2) Sector (of a circle)
3) 72
4) Segment (of a circle)
5) .375
6) One
7) Parabola
8) $2i$ or $-2i$
9) 2 by 2
10) 2 (golden ratio is approximately 1.618)

OPERATION DESERT STORM

Identify each of the following concerning Operation Desert Storm.

1) Year Iraq invaded and annexed Kuwait in August
2) Country to which President Bush then sent U.S. forces to discourage Iraqi attacks on its territory
3) Operation preceding Desert Storm
4) Iraqi leader
5) U.S. general who commanded the allied forces in the Persian Gulf
6) Long range rockets used by Iraqis
7) Name of the antimissile missiles employed by U.S. against these rockets
8) Cruise missiles U.S. used for the first time in warfare
9) Type of major fires started by the Iraqis
10) Full name of CNN, the organization that covered the war, sometimes live

Answers:

1) 1990
2) Saudi Arabia
3) Desert Shield
4) Saddam Hussein
5) Norman Schwarzkopf
6) Scuds
7) Patriot (missiles)
8) Tomahawk (Cruise missiles)
9) Oil fires
10) Cable News Network

U.S. PRESIDENTIAL ELECTION YEARS

Identify the year of each of the following from the given information.

1) Democrats Wilson and Marshall defeated Bull Moose Party Progressives Roosevelt and Johnson
2) Democrats Carter and Mondale defeated Republicans Ford and Dole
3) Republicans Lincoln and Hamlin defeated Independent Democrats Breckinridge and Lane
4) Republicans Harding and Coolidge defeated Democrats Cox and Roosevelt
5) Democrats Truman and Barkley defeated Republicans Dewey and Warren
6) Democrats Roosevelt and Truman defeated Republicans Dewey and Bricker
7) Republicans Eisenhower and Nixon defeated Democrats Stevenson and Sparkman
8) Republicans Bush and Quayle defeated Democrats Dukakis and Bentsen
9) Democrats Roosevelt and Garner defeated Republicans Landon and Knox
10) Republicans McKinley and Hobart defeated Democrats Jennings Bryan and Sewall

Answers:

1) 1912
2) 1976
3) 1860
4) 1920
5) 1948
6) 1944
7) 1952
8) 1988
9) 1936
10) 1896

BELLS

Identify each of the following associated with "bells."

1) American poet who wrote, "To the tintinnabulation that so musically wells / From the bells, bells, bells, bells"
2) Great bell in London's Parliament clock tower or the tower itself
3) English author who wrote, "And therefore never send to know for whom the bell tolls; it tolls for thee"
4) Admiral who said, "Damn the torpedoes! Four bells! . . . Full speed!" at the Battle of Mobile Bay
5) Bell ringer in Victor Hugo's *The Hunchback of Notre Dame*
6) Scottish-American who developed the telephone in 1876
7) Sylvia Plath's 1963 novel published under the pseudonym Victoria Lucas
8) Figure representing a symmetrical frequency distribution
9) Device that produces a strong current of air by sucking air through valves when expanded and then pumping it out when compressed
10) Disease that paralyzes one side of a person's face

Answers:

1) Edgar Allan Poe
2) Big Ben
3) John Donne
4) David G. Farragut
5) Quasimodo
6) Alexander G. Bell
7) *The Bell Jar*
8) Bell-shaped curve (accept bell curve)
9) Bellows
10) Bell's palsy

FAMOUS BATTLE SITES

Identify each of the following concerning famous battle sites.

1) Narrow pass in Greece where 300 Spartans under Leonidas held off the Persians in 480 B.C.
2) Cape off the coast of Spain where Lord Nelson defeated Napoleon's French navy in 1805
3) Plain in ancient Greece where the Athenians defeated the Persians in 490 B.C.
4) Egyptian site where Bernard Montgomery defeated the Field Marshal Erwin Rommel in 1942
5) French site where in 1415 Henry V of England defeated an army of French knights in the Hundred Years' War
6) Belgian site where the Duke of Wellington defeated Napoleon I in 1815
7) Texas site where General Santa Anna overran 183 Texans under Colonel Travis in 1836
8) Vietnam site where General Giap defeated French forces in 1954
9) Site where William the Conqueror defeated King Harold in 1066
10) River in France where French taxis moved troops from Paris to the front to thwart the Germans in 1914

Answers:

1) Thermopylae
2) Trafalgar
3) Marathon
4) El Alamein
5) Agincourt
6) Waterloo
7) Alamo
8) Dien Bien Phu
9) Hastings
10) Marne

THE LETTER *H*

Identify each of the following by giving an answer beginning with the letter *H*.

1) One of the Greater Antilles and the second-largest island in the West Indies
2) Greek known as "The Father of Medicine"
3) First in NASA's Great Observatory series, sent into space in April 1990
4) Term for the mass murder of European Jews by the Nazis during WWII
5) Greek god who gave Odysseus a magic herb to protect him from Circe's power
6) Composer of the *Messiah*
7) Acid whose formula is HCN
8) Hamlet's loyal friend from school
9) Poet who wrote "To an Athlete Dying Young"
10) Author of the short story "Young Goodman Brown"

Answers:

1) Hispaniola
2) Hippocrates
3) Hubble Space Telescope
4) Holocaust
5) Hermes
6) (George Frideric) Handel
7) Hydrocyanic acid
8) Horatio
9) (A.E.) Housman
10) (Nathaniel) Hawthorne

SCIENCE

Identify each of the following concerning science.

1) Geometrical figure with a major axis, a minor axis, and 2 foci, the curve made by Halley's comet as it orbits the sun
2) Only one of the 9 planets in our solar system not named for a Greek or Roman god
3) Sodium explodes violently when mixed with this substance, the most common one on earth
4) Name for a maneuver invented by a doctor for dislodging an object stuck in a windpipe
5) One of the 2 satellites of Mars
6) Name given to the high concentration of acids formed from gaseous pollutants and carried to the ground by precipitation
7) Term for the arrangement of the world's organisms into groups on the basis of their evolutionary or structural relationships
8) Term from the Greek for "opposite feet" designating two places that are exactly opposite each other on the globe
9) Planet known for its "Great Dark Spot," an Earth-sized cyclone
10) Name given to the maximum temperature at which a gas can be liquefied by pressure alone

Answers:

1) Ellipse
2) Earth
3) Water
4) Heimlich Maneuver (named after Dr. Heimlich)
5) Phobos or Deimos
6) Acid rain
7) Classification (also called taxonomy and systematics)
8) Antipodes
9) Neptune (NOTE: not to be confused with the "Great Red Spot" on Jupiter)
10) Critical temperature

QUICK MATH

Answer each of the following quick math questions.

1) Is the square root of 2 a whole number, a rational number, an irrational number, or an integer?
2) How many elements are in the range of the function $y = 4$?
3) What is 500% of 30?
4) In simplified form, what fractional part of a day is 20 hours?
5) How many degrees are equivalent to two *pi* radians?
6) What is the period of the tangent function?
7) Over the set of real numbers, what is the cube root of 343?
8) Which of the following is a geometric solid: dodecagon, icosahedron, trapezoid, or rhombus?
9) What is the name given to a quadrilateral with exactly 1 pair of parallel sides?
10) How many edges does a tetrahedron have?

Answers:

1) An irrational number
2) One (the set consisting of the element 4)
3) 150
4) 5/6 (do not accept 20/24)
5) 360 degrees
6) *Pi* (accept 180 degrees)
7) 7
8) Icosahedron
9) Trapezoid
10) 6 (edges)

LITERATURE

Identify each of the following concerning literature.

1) O. Henry short story in which a red-haired, freckle-faced ten-year-old boy is kidnapped in Alabama
2) State in which James Whitcomb Riley, "The Hoosier Poet," was born
3) Author of the *Aeneid*
4) Name that completes the line from Dickens' *A Christmas Carol*, "And so, as ____ observed, God Bless Us, Every One!"
5) Novel in which Phineas dies during surgery to set his broken leg
6) American author of *The Great Gatsby*
7) County included in the title of Mark Twain's story about a frog named Dan'l Webster
8) British author who created the fictional character Napoleon, the pig, in a 1941 novel
9) Fictional captain of the *Pequod* who is obsessed with the capture of Moby Dick, the great white whale
10) Title of the novel in which the character Rose of Sharon appears

Answers:

1) "The Ransom of Red Chief"
2) Indiana
3) Virgil
4) "Tiny Tim"
5) *A Separate Peace*
6) F. Scott Fitzgerald
7) Calaveras County (in "The Celebrated Jumping Frog of Calaveras County")
8) George Orwell
9) Captain Ahab
10) *The Grapes of Wrath*

ELECTIONS AND ELECTIONEERING

Identify each of the following concerning elections and electioneering.

1) Ballot on which a voter has voted candidates from more than one party
2) Mutual trading of favors by politicians, as by voting for each other's projects
3) Right to vote
4) Moving district lines in order to benefit one party
5) Declared principles of a party
6) System of rewarding supporters with appointment to political office after an election victory
7) Election which serves to select candidates for later elections
8) Voters served by an elected official
9) Putting a measure up for direct vote by the public
10) Vote to remove public official from office

Answer:

1) Split ticket
2) Logrolling
3) Suffrage (accept franchise)
4) Gerrymandering
5) Platform or plank
6) Spoils system
7) Primary
8) Constituency
9) Referendum
10) Recall

POETIC RHYME, METER, AND STRUCTURE

Identify each of the following concerning poetic rhyme, meter, and structure.

1) Poem's recurring rhythmic unit of stressed and unstressed syllables
2) Foot with one stressed then two unstressed syllables
3) Lyric poem with 14 lines
4) 4-line stanza
5) Foot with one unstressed then one stressed syllable
6) Unit of 2 or more lines making up one division of a poem
7) Unrhymed iambic pentameter verse
8) Poetry without any recurring foot
9) Foot with one stressed then one unstressed syllable
10) Poetic line with 6 iambic feet

Answer:

1) Foot
2) Dactyl foot
3) Sonnet
4) Quatrain
5) Iambic foot
6) Stanza
7) Blank verse
8) Free verse
9) Trochee (or trochaic foot)
10) Alexandrine

EDUCATORS

Identify each of the following educators.

1) Italian educator who founded a system to help children develop their intelligence and independence through play
2) Tennessee teacher on trial at the famed "Monkey Trial"
3) Helen Keller's teacher who helped her overcome her disabilities
4) Frenchman who invented the system of raised dots
5) Dewey who developed the Library Catalog System
6) Greek philosopher who tutored Plato
7) Greek philosopher who taught Alexander the Great
8) New Hampshire teacher who died in the explosion of the *Challenger* in 1986
9) Educator after whom the Columbia Institution for the Instruction of the Deaf, Dumb, and Blind in Washington, D.C., was renamed
10) Dewey who was the chief advocate of progressive education through his philosophy of instrumentalism

Answer:

1) Maria Montessori
2) John Scopes
3) Anne Sullivan (Macy)
4) Louis Braille
5) Melvil (Dewey)
6) Socrates
7) Aristotle
8) Christa McAuliffe
9) Thomas Hopkins Gallaudet
10) John (Dewey)

THE LETTER *I*

Identify each of the following by giving an answer beginning with the letter *I*.

1) John Greenleaf Whittier poem with the lines, "When faith is lost, when honor dies, / The man is dead!"
2) Modern country in which the ancient empire of Babylonia was located
3) Term for those pardons for sin whose sale was protested by Reformation leaders
4) U.S. state in which the Herbert Hoover Birthplace is located
5) Element named for the Greek goddess of the rainbow
6) League or confederation of Seneca, Mohawk, Oneida, Onondaga and Cayuga Indians
7) One of 2 or more kinds of atoms that usually have different atomic numbers but the same mass numbers
8) Current name of the Pennsylvania State House
9) U.S. capital city called "Crossroads of America" and located on the White River
10) Norwegian dramatist who wrote *A Doll's House*

Answers:

1) "Ichabod"
2) Iraq
3) Indulgences
4) Iowa
5) Iridium
6) Iroquois League
7) Isobars
8) Independence Hall
9) Indianapolis
10) (Henrik) Ibsen

LUNGS AND BREATHING

Identify each of the following concerning lungs and breathing.

1) Chronic disorder characterized by wheezing and difficulty in breathing, usually caused by allergy
2) Tiny, hairlike structures that push mucus upwards into the throat
3) Membrane that envelops the lungs and lines the chest cavity
4) Inflammation of the bronchial tubes
5) Communicable disease characterized by lesions in the lung tissues
6) One of the 5 large divisions that make up the lungs
7) Viral or bacterial infection of the lungs characterized by chills and high fever
8) Lung disease characterized by shortness of breath resulting from enlargement of the alveoli
9) Congenital disease, usually of childhood, characterized by the overproduction of mucus
10) Extremely rapid breathing with an intake of too much oxygen that may cause dizziness

Answers:

1) Asthma
2) Cilia
3) Pleura
4) Bronchitis
5) Tuberculosis
6) Lobe
7) Pneumonia
8) Emphysema
9) Cystic fibrosis
10) Hyperventilation

QUICK MATH

Identify each of the following quick math questions.

1) Geometric curve with equation $x^2/a^2 + y^2/b^2 = 1$ (x squared over a squared plus y squared over b squared equals one) where a and b are non-zero constant terms with a squared not equal to b squared
2) Union of the set of rational numbers and the set of irrational numbers
3) Property of real numbers stating that if A equals B, then B equals A
4) Plane figure which maximizes an area for a fixed perimeter
5) Principal square root of the product of 3, 6, and 2
6) Hours required for a 16-mile trip while travelling at an average speed of 5 miles per hour
7) Word used to describe a function whose range contains exactly one element
8) Another root of a polynomial with a root of $1 + 3i$ (one plus three i)
9) Minimum number of real roots of a nonconstant polynomial function with real coefficients and odd degree
10) Geometric curve with equation of the form $y = ax^2 + bx + c$ where a, b, and c are constant terms with a not equal to zero

Answers:

1) Ellipse
2) Real numbers (DO NOT ACCEPT complex numbers)
3) Symmetric (accept symmetric relation or symmetric property)
4) Circle
5) 6
6) 3 1/5 (or 3 hours 12 minutes, or 3.2 hours, or 16/5 hours)
7) Constant (function; accept many-to-one function; DO NOT ACCEPT horizontal line)
8) $1 - 3i$ (one minus three i)
9) One
10) Parabola

THE WORD *TIME*

Identify each of the following associated with the word *time*.

1) Author whose novel begins, "It was the best of times, it was the worst of times."
2) Largest divisions of the geologic time scale
3) Condition of being displaced from one point to another in time, as in science fiction
4) Time personified as an old man carrying a scythe and hourglass
5) Highest U.S. award given to civilians in peacetime, one first awarded in 1963
6) Washington Irving character who is hopelessly behind the times
7) English translation of the Latin *Tempus fugit*
8) Word for "the state or practice of having 2 or more wives or husbands at the same time"
9) Full name of DST, a year-round time adjustment first established in WWI
10) Country whose Time of Troubles from 1603-1613 was a period of civil war, invasion, and political turmoil

Answers:

1) Charles Dickens (*A Tale of Two Cities*)
2) Eras
3) Time warp (accept time travel)
4) Father Time
5) Presidential Medal of Freedom
6) Rip Van Winkle
7) Time flies (or time passes quickly)
8) Polygamy
9) Daylight Saving Time
10) Russia

WORLD HISTORY

Identify each of the following concerning world history.

1) European capital that was virtually destroyed by plague and fire in 1665-1666
2) 1898 war that ended Spanish rule of Cuba, Puerto Rico, and the Philippines
3) French leader who escaped from the island of Elba in 1815
4) Venetian who traveled throughout the Mongol Empire in the 13th century
5) 1919 treaty that ended WWI
6) Leader of the French army at the 1429 Battle of Orléans
7) Empire in Peru conquered by Francisco Pizarro in 16th century
8) Wars fought between Rome and Carthage from 264 to 146 B.C.
9) 18-year Asian war that ended in 1975
10) Carolingian king of the Franks who conquered much of western Europe in the 8th-9th century

Answers:

1) London
2) Spanish-American War
3) Napoleon (I; Bonaparte)
4) Marco Polo
5) Treaty of Versailles
6) Joan of Arc
7) Incan Empire
8) Punic Wars
9) Vietnam War
10) Charlemagne (accept Charles the Great and Charles I)

1992 ELECTION CAMPAIGN CITATIONS

Identify the person who said each of the following during the 1992 presidential election campaign.

1) "I tried marijuana as a graduate student in England but didn't like it and I didn't inhale."
2) "My dog Millie knows more about foreign affairs than those two bozos."
3) "I'm all ears."
4) "I suppose I could have stayed home and baked cookies and had teas."
5) "If he runs the country as well as he ran this campaign, we'll be all right."
6) "All I've been asked about by the press is a woman I didn't sleep with and a draft I didn't dodge."
7) "I knew Thomas Jefferson. Thomas Jefferson was a friend of mine, and Governor (Clinton), you're no Thomas Jefferson."
8) "Who am I? Why am I here?"
9) "There is a religious war going on in this country for the soul of America."
10) "We want . . . to see a working majority of the Republican Party in the hands of pro-family Christians by 1996."

Answers:

1) Bill Clinton
2) George Bush
3) Ross Perot
4) Hillary Clinton
5) Dan Quayle
6) Bill Clinton
7) Ronald Reagan
8) James Stockdale
9) Pat Buchanan
10) Pat Robertson

MUSEUMS IN CAPITAL CITIES

Identify the capital city for each of the following major museums.

1) Pompidou Center
2) MFA, or Museum of Fine Arts
3) Rijksmuseum
4) Victoria and Albert Museum
5) National Air and Space Museum
6) National Museum of India
7) High Museum of Art
8) Jeu de Paume
9) Isabella Stewart Gardner Museum
10) Capitoline Museum

Answers:

1) Paris
2) Boston
3) Amsterdam
4) London
5) Washington, D.C.
6) New Delhi
7) Atlanta
8) Paris
9) Boston
10) Rome

THE LETTER *J*

Identify each of the following by giving an answer including the letter *J*.

1) First U.S. President upon whose life an assassination attempt was made, occurring on January 30, 1835
2) Irish-born author of *Ulysses*
3) Famous chorus in George Frideric Handel's *Messiah*
4) Another term for Lower California
5) Willful telling of a lie while under oath
6) Korean city where an armistice was signed on July 27, 1953
7) Mountain that is Africa's highest
8) Wooden horse featured in Virgil's *Aeneid*
9) Term meaning *enlightened rule* that identifies the period in Japan from 1867 to 1912
10) Trench that is the deepest part in the Indian Ocean

Answers:

1) (Andrew) Jackson
2) (James) Joyce
3) "Hallelujah"
4) Baja California (Baja Peninsula)
5) Perjury
6) Panmunjom
7) (Mount) Kilimanjaro
8) Trojan Horse
9) Meiji Period
10) Java Trench

STRAITS

Identify each of the following concerning straits.

1) One between Siberia and Alaska named after the Danish explorer employed by Russia who discovered Alaska
2) Englishman after whom a river, a bay, and a strait in North America are named
3) One in the English Channel between England and France
4) One that connects Lakes Michigan and Huron
5) One that connects the Black Sea with the Sea of Marmara
6) One that is the Persian Gulf's only outlet to the sea
7) One joining the Aegean Sea with the Sea of Marmara and formerly called the *Hellespont*
8) One at extreme end of South America between mainland and Tierra del Fuego Archipelago
9) Strait between Greenland and Canada named for the Englishman who discovered it
10) One that separates the Malay Peninsula from the Indonesian island of Sumatra

Answers:

1) Bering (after Vitus Jonassen Bering)
2) Henry Hudson
3) Strait of Dover (Straits of Dover or Pas de Calais)
4) Straits of Mackinac
5) Bosporus
6) Strait of Hormuz
7) Dardanelles
8) Strait of Magellan
9) Davis Strait
10) Strait of Malacca

QUICK MATH

Answer each of the following quick math questions.

1) If each step in a staircase is 12 inches high, how many steps are in a staircase 15 feet high?
2) What number is the additive identity for all real numbers?
3) What name is given to the graph of $y^2 - x^2 = 4$?
4) What is the square root of 64 times the square root of 16?
5) Over the set of real numbers, what is the domain of the following function: $y = 7x - 4$?
6) With which one of the conic sections are the transverse axis, conjugate axis, and asymptotes associated?
7) Over the set of real numbers, what number is excluded from the domain of the following function: $y = 1/x$ (READ: y equals one over x)?
8) What is the name of the graph of the equation $y^2 + x^2 = 1$?
9) What is the logarithm of 1/25 (READ: one twenty-fifth) to the base 5?
10) If a watch loses 10 seconds in an hour, how many minutes will it lose in 24 hours?

Answers:

1) 15
2) 0 (zero)
3) Hyperbola
4) 32
5) All real numbers
6) Hyperbola
7) 0 (zero)
8) Circle
9) Negative 2
10) 4 (minutes)

U.S. CONSTITUTION

Identify each of the following concerning the U.S. Constitution.

1) Two delegates to the Constitutional Convention who became U.S. Presidents
2) Minimum age set for the U.S. President
3) Person, whose first name is Gouverneur, who polished the language of the Constitution
4) Three independent branches of government established by Constitution
5) Person who served as President of the Constitutional Convention
6) Phrase for what *Marbury v. Madison* established in 1803 as the Supreme Court's power to declare a law unconstitutional
7) First state to ratify the document on December 7, 1787
8) Name given to those who favored ratification
9) Number of years each state has to consider amendment changes
10) Amendment that guarantees trial by jury in federal courts for civil actions in amounts for more than $20

Answers:

1) George Washington and James Madison
2) 35
3) Gouverneur Morris
4) Executive, legislative, and judicial
5) George Washington
6) Judicial review
7) Delaware
8) Federalists
9) 7 years
10) 7th Amendment

FRENCH PHRASES

Give the English for each of the following French phrases.

1) *avoir froid*
2) *avoir peur de*
3) *avoir chaud*
4) *avoir besoin de*
5) *avoir tort*
6) *avoir sommeil*
7) *avoir faim*
8) *avoir soif*
9) *à l'heure*
10) *à gauche*

Answers:

1) To be cold
2) To be afraid of
3) To be hot
4) To need
5) To be wrong
6) To be sleepy
7) To be hungry
8) To be thirsty
9) On time
10) On the left

U.S. INAUGURATION POTPOURRI

Identify each of the following concerning U.S. inaugurations.

1) President who said, "A new breeze is blowing—and a nation refreshed by freedom stands ready to push on."
2) Only President who took the oath of office in 2 different cities
3) Poet who recited "The Gift Outright" at Kennedy's inauguration
4) President who went coatless during his inauguration, spoke for almost 2 hours, and later died of pneumonia
5) Only President sworn in by his father
6) President who said, "The torch has been passed to a new generation of Americans, born in this century."
7) Oldest Vice President inaugurated, one who served under Truman from 1949 to 1953
8) President who said, "This is our time. Let us embrace it."
9) President whose inauguration in 1921 was the first to be broadcast live on radio
10) Poet who recited "On the Pulse of Morning" at Clinton's inauguration

Answers:

1) George Bush
2) George Washington
3) Robert Frost
4) William H. Harrison
5) Calvin Coolidge
6) John F. Kennedy
7) Alben Barkley
8) Bill Clinton
9) Warren Harding
10) Maya Angelou

LETTERS AND/OR NUMBERS

Give the letters or combination of letters and numbers representing the following.

1) World's 2nd highest mountain
2) Quantity 2.71828
3) August 15, 1945 or September 2, 1945
4) Please respond
5) Hawthorne's scarlet letter
6) May 8, 1945
7) June 6, 1944
8) Planck's constant
9) Water formula
10) Equivalent of or equals mc^2

Answers:

1) K-2
2) *e*
3) V-J Day (fighting ended with Japan on August 15, 1945 / surrender was formally accepted on September 2, 1945)
4) RSVP
5) A
6) V-E Day
7) D-Day
8) h
9) H_2O
10) E

THE LETTER *K*

Identify each of the following by giving an answer ending in the letter *K*.

1) Biblical vessel that may have landed on Mount Ararat in northeastern Turkey
2) Quasimodo's deformity
3) Name for any group of hypothetical particles believed by some to be the basis of all matter in the universe
4) Russian author of *Doctor Zhivago*
5) War during which Abraham Lincoln served for 90 days in 1832
6) Rough, rowdy fight, like a riotous fair once held near Dublin
7) U.S. capital with a German proper name
8) Shakespearean character who enjoys playing pranks on human beings and who says, "Lord, what fools these mortals be!"
9) New Jersey city of which Thomas Edison was known as the "Wizard"
10) Young girl whose secret diary was written in Amsterdam, The Netherlands

Answers:

1) Noah's Ark
2) Hunchback
3) Quark
4) (Boris) Pasternak
5) Black Hawk (War)
6) Donnybrook (from Donnybrook Fair)
7) Bismarck (North Dakota)
8) Puck
9) ("Wizard of") Menlo Park
10) (Anne) Frank

DIGESTIVE SYSTEM

Identify each of the following concerning the digestive system.

1) Substance that forms the major part of the cell walls of vegetables and serves as bulk for the large intestines
2) Word from the Greek for "bad digestion"
3) Word from the Greek for "leavened" for a catalyst that helps digest food
4) Of the 3 main classes of nutrients, the one that is the body's most efficient form of stored fuel
5) Burning sensation in the esophagus resulting from stomach acid
6) Muscular tube made up of the caecum and the ascending, transverse, descending, and sigmoid portions of the colon
7) First portion of the small intestine
8) Inflammation of the tube attached to the caecum of the colon
9) Inflammation of the colon
10) Chronic form of diabetes, mainly caused by the insufficient production of insulin by the pancreas

Answers:

1) Cellulose
2) Dyspepsia
3) Enzyme
4) Fat
5) Heartburn (accept pyrosis and brash)
6) Large intestine
7) Duodenum
8) Appendicitis
9) Colitis
10) Diabetes mellitus

RADICALS AND EXPONENTS

Simplify each of the following expressions if a and b represent positive numbers and $i = \sqrt{-1}$.

1) $\sqrt{(a^2b^4)}$ [square root of quantity a squared times b to the fourth power]
2) $16^{3/4}$ [sixteen to the three-fourths power]
3) $(a^3b^2)^5$ [quantity a cubed times b squared all raised to the fifth power]
4) $(1/5)^{-2}$ [one fifth to the negative two power]
5) $(a^6b^{12})^{1/3}$ [quantity a to the 6th power times b to the 12th power all raised to the one-third power]
6) 1^{10} [one to the tenth power]
7) $\sqrt[3]{(-8a^9b^3)}$ [cube root of quantity negative 8 to the ninth power times b cubed]
8) $(a^{-4})^{-3/4}$ [quantity a to the negative four power raised to the negative three fourths power]
9) $\sqrt[3]{(\sqrt{64})}$ [cube root of the square root of sixty-four]
10) $4\sqrt{28} \div 3\sqrt{7}$ [four times the square root of 28 divided by the quantity three times the square root of seven]

Answers:

1) ab^2
2) 8 (accept 2 cubed)
3) $a^{15}b^{10}$
4) 25 (accept 5 squared)
5) a^2b^4
6) 1
7) $-2a^3b$
8) a^3
9) 2
10) 8/3 (accept 2 2/3)

A *BEAR*ABLE CATEGORY

Identify each of the following concerning *bears*.

1) Army General nicknamed "The Bear" who commanded U.S. Middle East forces in 1990-1991
2) Word ending in "ine," meaning "bearlike"
3) Bear known as *Ursus (thalarctos) maritimus*
4) Chicago Bears player that is the subject of the 1971 film *Brian's Song*
5) Wyoming-born abstract expressionistic painter known for *Reflection of the Great Bear* (or *Big Dipper*)
6) Character in many children's stories whose name is derived from an old Dutch word for "brown"
7) Latin name for the constellation known as the Little Bear
8) Alabama football coach, nicknamed "the Bear," who retired with 323 career victories
9) Bear known as *Ursus (arctos) horribilis*
10) Founder and great coach of the Chicago Bears known as "Papa Bear"

Answers:

1) H. Norman Schwarzkopf
2) Ursine
3) Polar bear
4) Brian Piccolo
5) Jackson Pollock
6) Bruin
7) Ursa Minor
8) Paul "Bear" Bryant
9) Grizzly bear
10) George Halas

HORNS

Identify each of the following concerning *horns*.

1) Name given to the family of wind instruments including horns, trombones, trumpets, and tubas
2) Present-day U.S. state where Little Big Horn is located
3) Two countries that make up Cape Horn
4) Dinosaur whose name is derived from the Greek for "three-horned eye (face)"
5) More common name for the wild sheep of North America, the males of which have curling horns
6) Play in which the horn on Laura's glass unicorn is broken
7) Stiff, horny material that makes up the exoskeleton of arthropods
8) Colorful name given to the arm of the Bosporus that forms the harbor of Istanbul
9) City in which the Hirshhorn Museum is located
10) Mythological woodland deity with pointed ears, short horns, the head and body of a man, and the legs of a goat or horse

Answers:

1) Brass
2) Montana
3) Chile and Argentina
4) Triceratops
5) Bighorn sheep
6) *The Glass Menagerie*
7) Chitin
8) Golden Horn
9) Washington, D.C.
10) Satyr

FAMOUS ROBERTS

Identify each of the following famous Roberts.

1) Explorer who claimed that on April 6, 1909, he became the first man to reach the North Pole
2) American author of *All the King's Men*
3) Secretary of Defense during the Kennedy administration
4) German physician who established bacteriology as a separate science
5) Scottish botanist who in 1827 described the erratic motion of microscopic particles suspended in a fluid
6) First black Cabinet member, the Secretary of Housing and Urban Development appointed by Lyndon Johnson
7) Georgian who was the first and only golfer to win the Grand Slam of Golf
8) British founder of the Boy Scouts
9) British poet laureate and author of the ballad "The Battle of Blenheim"
10) Naval captain aboard the *Columbia* who became the first to circumnavigate the globe on an American ship

Answers:

1) Robert Peary
2) Robert Penn Warren
3) Robert Strange McNamara
4) Robert Koch
5) Robert Brown (Brownian motion or movement)
6) Robert C. Weaver
7) Robert (Bobby) Tyre Jones, Jr.
8) Sir Robert Baden-Powell
9) Robert Southey
10) Robert Gray

LATIN WORDS AND PHRASES

Give the English for each of the following Latin words.

1) *modus operandi*
2) *ante meridiem*
3) *circa*
4) *anno domini*
5) *exempli gratia*
6) *et alii*
7) *et cetera*
8) *ibidem*
9) *id est*
10) *confer*

Answers:

1) mode of operation
2) before noon
3) about
4) in the year of our Lord
5) for example
6) and others
7) and others; and the like; and so forth
8) in the same place
9) that is
10) compare

THE LETTER *L*

Identify each of the following by giving an answer beginning with the letter *L*.

1) Band of strong, flexible tissue that holds organs in place and connects bones together
2) Norwegian city that was awarded the 1994 Winter Olympic Games
3) Organ of the human body affected by hepatitis
4) Brother of Ophelia in Shakespeare's *Hamlet*
5) Abraham's biblical nephew whose wife was turned into a pillar of salt
6) 18th-19th century French statesman and general known as "the Hero of Two Worlds"
7) Mother of Pollux and Helen by Zeus who allegedly came to her in the shape of a swan
8) Full name of the acronym LASER
9) Author of the short story "The Rocking-Horse Winner"
10) Author of the novel *Elmer Gantry*

Answers:

1) Ligament
2) Lillehammer
3) Liver
4) Laertes
5) Lot
6) (Marquis de) Lafayette
7) Leda
8) Light Amplification by Stimulated Emission of Radiation
9) (D.H.) Lawrence
10) (Sinclair) Lewis

NEW FROM *BARTLETT'S FAMILIAR QUOTATIONS*

Identify the person who made each of the following statements included in the 16th edition of *Bartlett's Familiar Quotations*.

1) "The Congress will push me to raise taxes, and I'll say no, no, . . . and they'll push again. And all I can say to them is read my lips: No New Taxes."
2) "Honey, I just forgot to duck."
3) "It's not that easy bein' green."
4) "I meant what I said / And I said what I meant . . . / An elephant's faithful / one hundred per cent!"
5) "We're more popular than Jesus now. I don't know which will go first—rock 'n' roll or Christianity."
6) "We have a cancer within, close to the Presidency, that is growing."
7) "I would like a medium Vodka dry Martini—with a slice of lemon peel. Shaken and not stirred, please."
8) "That's the news from Lake Wobegon, where all the women are strong, the men are good-looking, and all the children are above average."
9) "I can't get no respect."
10) "I had felt for a long time, that if I was ever told to get up so a white person could sit, that I would refuse to do so."

Answers:

1) George Bush
2) Ronald Reagan (accept Jack Dempsey)
3) Kermit the Frog (sung by him)
4) Dr. Seuss (Theodor Seuss Geisel; in *Horton Hatches the Egg*)
5) John Lennon
6) John Dean
7) Ian Fleming (accept James Bond)
8) Garrison Keillor
9) Rodney Dangerfield
10) Rosa Parks

THEATRE LANGUAGE

Identify the following terms taken from the field of theatre.

1) Part of stage on the right or left side of the stage proper
2) 20th century variety theatre
3) Arch separating the audience from the stage
4) Wordless theatrical performance
5) Group paid to cheer and applaud a performance
6) Conversation between characters
7) Latin phrase for a list of players in a cast
8) Japanese drama with masked players
9) Japanese theatre with all male dancing
10) Area of a theatre for use of actors when they are waiting off stage

Answers:

1) Wings
2) Vaudeville
3) Proscenium (or proscenium arch)
4) Pantomime
5) Claque
6) Dialogue
7) *Dramatis personae*
8) Noh (or No) theatre (also called Nogaku)
9) Kabuki
10) Greenroom

ANSWERS WITH DOUBLE LETTERS

Identify each of the following with an answer that includes a doubling of the given letter.

1) N - Term designating the idea suggested by a word or phrase beyond its dictionary meaning or denotation
2) M - German brothers who collaborated to publish their *Fairy Tales*
3) L - Disease the World Health Organization announced in 1979 had been wiped out
4) O - Famous 1815 battle fought in Belgium
5) P - Human body part, often described as vermiform and considered to be vestigial
6) R - 1984 Democratic vice presidential candidate to Walter Mondale
7) B - Baseball player known as "The Georgia Peach"
8) T - Owner of Sacramento Valley sawmill where James Marshall discovered gold in 1848
9) A - Official language of South Africa other than English
10) S - Priam's daughter who was given the gift of prophecy by Apollo

Answers:

1) Connotation
2) Brothers Grimm (accept Grimm)
3) Smallpox
4) Waterloo
5) Appendix (the vermiform appendix)
6) Geraldine Ferraro
7) Ty Cobb
8) John Sutter
9) Afrikaans
10) Cassandra

U.S. PRESIDENTIAL ELECTION YEARS

Identify each of the following U.S. Presidential years from the given information.

1) Republicans Roosevelt and Fairbanks defeated Democrats Parker and Davis
2) Democrats Roosevelt and Wallace defeated Republicans Willkie and McNary
3) Republicans Nixon and Agnew defeated Democrats Humphrey and Muskie
4) Republicans Coolidge and Dawes defeated Democrats Davis and Bryan
5) Republicans Taft and Sherman defeated Democrats Bryan and Kern
6) Republicans McKinley and Roosevelt defeated Democrats Bryan and Stevenson
7) Democrats Wilson and Marshall defeated Republicans Hughes and Fairbanks
8) Democrats Roosevelt and Garner defeated Republicans Hoover and Curtis
9) Republicans Eisenhower and Nixon defeated Democrats Stevenson and Kefauver
10) Republicans Reagan and Bush defeated Democrats Carter and Mondale

Answers:

1) 1904
2) 1940
3) 1968
4) 1924
5) 1908
6) 1900
7) 1916
8) 1932
9) 1956
10) 1980

AFRICAN-AMERICAN LITERATURE

Identify each of the following concerning African-American literature.

1) African country, the former "Gold Coast," where Maya Angelou seeks her roots in the autobiography *All God's Children Need Traveling Shoes*
2) Author who assisted Malcolm X in writing his autobiography
3) Letter-writing narrator and protagonist of Alice Walker's 1983 Pulitzer novel *The Color Purple*
4) Playwright who won both a Tony Award and a Pulitzer for his 1985 play *Fences*
5) Author of the rites-of-passage autobiographical novel *Go Tell It on the Mountain*
6) Ralph Ellison's 1952 novel considered by some an African-American's *Pilgrim's Progress*
7) First African-American to win the Pulitzer Prize for poetry
8) 20-year-old protagonist of Richard Wright's *Native Son*
9) Alex Haley's West African forefather whose life story takes up almost two-thirds of the book *Roots*
10) Poet from whose verse "Harlem" Lorraine Hansberry took the title of her play *A Raisin in the Sun*

Answers:

1) Ghana
2) Alex Haley
3) Celie
4) August Wilson
5) James Baldwin
6) *Invisible Man*
7) Gwendolyn Brooks
8) Bigger Thomas
9) Kunta Kinte
10) Langston Hughes

MYTHOLOGICAL PAIRS

Complete each of the following famous mythological pairs.

1) Romulus and _________
2) Hero and _________
3) Damon and _________
4) Orpheus and _________
5) Castor and _________
6) Penelope and _________
7) Cupid and _________
8) Lares and _________
9) Pyramus and _________
10) Phrixus and _________

Answers:

1) Remus
2) Leander
3) Pythias
4) Eurydice
5) Pollux
6) Odysseus (Ulysses)
7) Psyche
8) Penates
9) Thisbe
10) Helle

THE LETTER *M*

Identify each of the following by giving an answer beginning with the letter *M*.

1) "Most Noble Mountain of the Alps" in the Pennine Alps on the Swiss-Italian border
2) Home of Thomas Jefferson located near Charlottesville, Virginia
3) Composer of the opera *Così Fan Tutte*
4) Latin plural of "wise man," a word meaning wizard in the Persian language
5) Process through which the larvae of amphibians change into adults
6) Guerilla commander during the Revolutionary War known as the "Swamp Fox"
7) 16th century Flemish cartographer known as "The Father of Modern Geography"
8) Term for a weather forecaster
9) New England capital that is the least populous in the U.S.
10) Hereditary disorder characterized by long, lean limbs, unsteady gait, and stooping shoulders

Answers:

1) Matterhorn (accept Mont Cervin or Monte Cervino)
2) Monticello
3) (Wolfgang Amadeus) Mozart
4) Magi (Magus is the singular)
5) Metamorphosis
6) (Francis) Marion
7) (Gerardus) Mercator
8) Meteorologist
9) Montpelier (Vermont)
10) Marfan's syndrome (or Marfan syndrome)

MIND AND PERSONALITY

Identify the following associated with psychology, psychiatry or parapsychology.

1) Lack of conscious awareness of one's behavior or surrounding events
2) In Freudian theory, part of the psyche involving moral standards, conscience, and guilt
3) Tendency to withdraw from others and focus attention inward on the self
4) In Freudian theory, part of the psyche dominated by the pleasure principle
5) In Freudian theory, part of the psyche that experiences the external world through the senses
6) C.G. Jung theory for the inherited psychic experience shared by a society or people
7) Another aspect of oneself
8) Area of mental activity occurring below the level of conscious realization
9) Response occasioned by a secondary stimulus
10) General psychic energy, specifically the sexual desire

Answers:

1) Unconscious
2) Superego
3) Introversion
4) Id
5) Ego
6) Collective unconscious
7) Alter ego
8) Subconscious
9) Conditioned response (or reflex or conditioning)
10) Libido

CITIES IN WHICH MUSEUMS ARE LOCATED

Identify the city, a non-capital one, in which each of the following major museums is located.

1) The Solomon R. Guggenheim Museum
2) J. Paul Getty Museum
3) Uffizi Gallery
4) Field Museum of Natural History
5) Museum of Modern Art
6) Hermitage
7) Royal Ontario Museum
8) Salvador Dali Museum
9) Hagia Sophia
10) Metropolitan Museum of Art

Answers:

1) New York
2) Malibu (California)
3) Florence
4) Chicago
5) New York
6) Saint Petersburg (formerly Leningrad; Russia)
7) Toronto
8) Saint Petersburg (Florida)
9) Istanbul
10) New York

WOMEN HONORED BY U.S. POSTAL STAMPS

Identify each of the following women honored by U.S. postal stamps.

1) Founder of the Girl Scouts in the U.S., in Savannah, Georgia, in 1912
2) Grandmother who began painting her primitive pictures in her 70s
3) New York women's rights advocate honored by a U.S. dollar coin
4) U.S. delegate to the U.N. appointed by President Truman in 1945
5) Hull House founder and co-winner of 1931 Nobel Peace Prize
6) Author of *Death Comes for the Archbishop* and *My Antonia*
7) First American woman to win a Nobel Prize for literature, in 1938
8) Author who wrote "Battle Hymn of the Republic"
9) Civil War nurse who wrote *Little Women* in 1869
10) First woman Cabinet member, appointed secretary of labor in 1933

Answers:

1) Juliette G. Low
2) Grandma Moses (accept Anna Mary Robertson)
3) Susan B. Anthony
4) Eleanor Roosevelt
5) Jane Addams
6) Willa Cather
7) Pearl Buck
8) Julia Ward Howe
9) Louisa May Alcott
10) Frances Perkins

DOUBLE *S*

Identify the following by giving an answer that includes a double *S*.

1) "Father of Waters"
2) "Show-Me State"
3) Italian dictator
4) *North Star* founder
5) Coleridge bird
6) *Glasnost* meaning
7) Whooping cough
8) "Volunteer State"
9) Hydrocyanic acid
10) Last Spandau prisoner

Answers:

1) Mississippi
2) Missouri
3) (Benito) Mussolini
4) (Frederick) Douglass
5) Albatross
6) Openness
7) Pertussis
8) Tennessee
9) Prussic acid
10) (Rudolf) Hess

COMPLETION OF PHRASES WITH PROPER NAMES

Give the word that accompanies each of the following proper names to form an expression in common use today.

1) Oedipus ________
2) Fallopian ________
3) Molotov ________
4) Mercator ________
5) Hobson's ________
6) Freudian ________
7) Cardigan ________
8) Midas ________
9) Napier's ________
10) Graham ________

Answers:

1) complex
2) tube
3) cocktail (breadbasket)
4) projection
5) choice
6) slip
7) sweater
8) touch
9) bones (accept logarithm)
10) cracker

MADE OF IRON

Identify the following, each of which is associated with the word *iron*.

1) Erich Maria Remarque novel about "Iron Youth" or German soldiers of WWI
2) Name for the "gold" called pyrite, or iron pyrite
3) M-initialled Minnesota range with iron deposits
4) Two ironclad ships that fought on March 9, 1862, at the Battle of Hampton Roads
5) Chemical symbol for Iron
6) Two of the 3 events in Ironman Triathlons
7) "Iron Lady" who resigned as prime minister of Great Britain in 1990
8) Murderous Russian dictator known as "Iron Joe," who served from 1928 to 1953
9) British general known as the "Iron Duke"
10) Country that awards the Iron Cross, a medal for outstanding bravery during wartime

Answers:

1) *All Quiet on the Western Front*
2) Fool's gold
3) Mesabi
4) USS *Monitor* and the CSS *Virginia* (accept *Merrimack*)
5) Fe
6) (2.4 mile ocean) *swim*, (112-mile) *bicycle trip*, and *marathon run*
7) Margaret Thatcher
8) Joseph Stalin
9) Duke of Wellington (or Arthur Wellesley)
10) Germany

THE LETTER *N*

Identify each of the following by giving an answer beginning with the letter *N*.

1) Phrase Bill Clinton borrowed from the Bible for the new commitment he seeks between people and the government
2) English admiral who said, "England expects every man will do his duty."
3) Gas whose chemical formula is N_2O
4) Capital city called "Music City, USA," the home of the Grand Ole Opry
5) Branch of medicine dealing with the nervous system, its structure, and its diseases
6) Term designating any nerve cell
7) Country whose South Island is the larger of the 2 main islands
8) Country whose former name was South West Africa
9) Group of free-swimming marine organisms
10) Death or decay of cells or body tissues due to disease

Answers:

1) New Covenant
2) (Horatio) Nelson
3) Nitrous oxide
4) Nashville
5) Neurology
6) Neuron
7) New Zealand
8) Namibia
9) Nekton
10) Necrosis

ALL ABOUT STRIKES

Identify the following, each of which is associated with the word *strike*.

1) Minimum number of strikeouts if a pitcher struck out every batter for a perfect game in major league baseball
2) Number of strikes needed to bowl 300
3) U.S. President who seized control of the steel mills on April 8, 1952, in order to prevent their shutdown by strikers
4) U.S. President who ordered military strikes on Iraq during his last week in office
5) U.S. President during the longest steel strike, from July 15, 1959, to January 4, 1960
6) Texas Ranger who was first pitcher in major league baseball to strike out 5,000 batters
7) Acronym of striking air traffic controllers, early 1980s
8) U.S. President who sent in troops to break the 1894 Pullman strike on grounds that U.S. mail delivery was being obstructed
9) Conductor who wrote music for *The Empire Strikes Back*
10) Governor who said during the 1919 Boston police strike, "There is no right to strike against the public safety by anybody, anywhere, anytime"

Answers:

1) 27
2) 12
3) Harry S Truman
4) George Bush
5) Dwight Eisenhower
6) Nolan Ryan
7) PATCO
8) Grover Cleveland
9) John Williams
10) Calvin Coolidge

GRAPHS AND THE COORDINATE PLANE

Identify each of the following.

1) Coordinates of the vertex of the parabola $y = x^2$
2) Domain of the greatest integer function
3) Slope of a vertical line
4) Quadrants in which the graph of $yx^2 = 1$ (y times x squared equals one) appears
5) Name for a point of intersection of a graph and the x-axis
6) Equation of the y-axis
7) Distance between the points (5,0) and (–7,0)
8) Slope of a horizontal line
9) Radius of the circle with equation $x^2 + y^2 = 10$
10) 17th century French mathematician who helped invent coordinate geometry

Answers:

1) (0,0)
2) Set of real numbers (accept reals or all real numbers)
3) Undefined (no value; no slope)
4) 1 and 2 (both numbers required)
5) Intercept (or x-intercept)
6) $x = 0$ (Do NOT accept 0)
7) 12
8) 0
9) Square root of 10
10) (René) Descartes

HISTORY

Identify each of the following concerning history.

1) Term that designates the period in American history following the Civil War from 1865 to 1877
2) Spanish leaders represented by the initials F and I on the seal of Puerto Rico
3) U.S. President who said at the Berlin Wall, "Ich bin ein Berliner"
4) U.S. President in 1917 who said that "the world must be made safe for democracy"
5) U.S. President when Alaska was purchased in 1867
6) Russian premier in 1961 when the Berlin Wall was erected
7) King of England when George Washington was inaugurated in 1789
8) University Thomas Jefferson founded in 1819
9) Cuban site of the failed April 17, 1961, U.S.-backed invasion to overthrow Fidel Castro
10) British explorer after whose first ship the space shuttle *Endeavour* was named

Answers:

1) Reconstruction
2) Ferdinand and Isabella
3) John Kennedy
4) Woodrow Wilson
5) Andrew Johnson
6) Nikita Khrushchev
7) George III
8) University of Virginia
9) Bay of Pigs
10) Captain James Cook

FAMOUS PAIRS

Complete each of the following famous pairs.

1) Currier and _________
2) Lewis and _________
3) Mason and _________
4) Dante and _________
5) Abelard and _________
6) Rosencrantz and _________
7) Marquette and _________
8) Rodgers and _________
9) Gilbert and _________
10) Stanley and _________

Answers:

1) Ives
2) Clark
3) Dixon
4) Beatrice
5) Heloise (Héloïse)
6) Gildenstern
7) Joliett (Jolliet)
8) Hammerstein
9) Sullivan
10) Livingstone

GEOGRAPHY

Identify each of the following concerning geography.

1) Excluding Brazil, one of the other 2 South American countries crossed by the equator
2) World's 6th-largest country, a federation of 6 states
3) Largest New England state in area
4) European capital known as the "The Eternal City"
5) U.S. capital city, called the "Dogwood City," originally named Terminus, then Marthasville
6) World's largest freshwater lake
7) One of the 2 South American countries that do not border Brazil
8) One of the 2 U.S. capital cities with a 2-word name beginning with the letter *S*
9) Freshwater lake that is the world's second largest and Africa's largest
10) One of the 2 landlocked countries of South America

Answers:

1) Colombia or Ecuador
2) Australia
3) Maine
4) Rome
5) Atlanta (Georgia)
6) Lake Superior
7) Chile or Ecuador
8) St. Paul or Santa Fe
9) Lake Victoria (accept Victoria Nyanza)
10) Bolivia or Paraguay

POSSESSIVES

Identify the following, each of which includes an apostrophe *s*.

1) Robert Penn Warren's 1947 Pulitzer Prize-winning novel based on the life of Huey Long, a Louisiana politician
2) Fictitious stories with a moral lesson by Greek fabulist of 6th century B.C.
3) 1678 religious allegory by John Bunyan
4) Mountain in central Colorado discovered by an explorer whose first name was Zebulon
5) Parliamentary procedures in a book published in 1876 by a U.S. major
6) Book of synonyms and antonyms by English writer Peter Mark Roget
7) Contagious fungal infection found on the feet
8) Epic Civil War poem by Stephen Vincent Benét
9) Boy's magical container by which he summons a genie to do his bidding in *The Arabian Nights*
10) Famous painting more properly entitled *Arrangement in Gray and Black No.1*

Answers:

1) *All the King's Men*
2) *Aesop's Fables*
3) *Pilgrim's Progress*
4) Pike's Peak
5) *Robert's Rules of Order*
6) *Roget's Thesaurus*
7) Athlete's foot
8) John Brown's Body
9) Aladdin's lamp
10) Whistler's mother (accept Artist's mother)

THE LETTER *O*

Identify each of the following by giving an answer beginning with the letter *O*.

1) Thornton Wilder play featuring Simon Stimson, Howie Newsome, and Constable Warren
2) Cereal plants of the grass family, native to Eurasia
3) King of the Norse gods who with his brothers killed the first living being
4) Indian leader who led the Seminoles against U.S. troops in the mid-1830s
5) Cranial nerve that carries the sensation of smell from the nose to the brain
6) Name of y-coordinate of a point (x,y) in the Cartesian coordinate plane
7) Collective name for the 10,000 small islands in the Pacific Ocean between Asia and America
8) U.S. capital city with Mt. Rainier and the Olympic Mountains within its view
9) Surname of the second husband of Jacqueline Kennedy
10) In Greek religion, priest or priestess, who revealed god's answer to a human questioner

Answers:

1) *Our Town*
2) Oats
3) Odin
4) Osceola
5) Olfactory nerve
6) Ordinate
7) Oceania (or Oceanica)
8) Olympia (Washington)
9) (Aristotle Socrates) Onassis
10) Oracle

STICKS AND STONES

Identify the following, each of which is associated with either "sticks" or "stones."

1) Location of the Butcher, Baker, and Candlestick-maker in the nursery rhyme "Rub-a-dub-dub"
2) Dwight Stones's Olympic event, same as Dick Fosbury's
3) U.S. President with the "Big Stick" foreign policy
4) Subject of Irving Stone's *The Agony and the Ecstasy*
5) City in which Candlestick Park is the home of the 49ers and Giants
6) National park located in Wyoming, Montana, and Idaho
7) U.S. state capital city whose name means "Red Stick" in French
8) U.S. state in which the Stone Mountain monument is located
9) Don McLean song that includes the words "Jack Flash sat on a candlestick / and fire was the devil's only friend"
10) English plain on which England's Stonehenge is found

Answers:

1) In a tub
2) High jump
3) Theodore Roosevelt
4) Michelangelo
5) San Francisco
6) Yellowstone National Park
7) Baton Rouge
8) Georgia
9) "American Pie"
10) Salisbury

FATHERLY NICKNAMES

Identify the following so-called "fathers."

1) 19th century American publisher of *The Liberator* known as "The Father of Abolitionism"
2) 18th century American President known as "The Father of His Country"
3) 20th century Swiss known as "The Father of Analytic Psychology"
4) 4th century B.C. Greek known as "The Father of Comedy"
5) 14th century poet known as "The Father of English Poetry"
6) 5th century B.C. Athenian playwright known as "The Father of Greek Tragedy"
7) 18th century Frenchman known as "The Father of Modern Chemistry"
8) 5th century B.C. Greek known as "The Father of History"
9) 20th century spiritual leader known as "The Father of India"
10) 16th century Fleming known as "The Father of Modern Geography"

Answers:

1) William Lloyd Garrison
2) George Washington
3) Carl Gustav Jung
4) Aristophanes
5) Geoffrey Chaucer
6) Aeschylus (accept Thespis)
7) Antoine Lavoisier
8) Herodotus
9) Mohandas "Mahatma" Gandhi
10) Gerardus Mercator (accept Gerhard Kremer)

DOUBLE NAMES BEGINNING WITH THE LETTER *S*

Identify the following by giving 2-word answers, both of which begin with the letter *S*.

1) That portion of our galaxy which is subject to the gravity of the sun
2) Area of the Atlantic Ocean noted for its surface gulfweed
3) First director of the Peace Corps
4) Phrase for all the oceans of the world
5) Assassin of Robert Kennedy
6) Capital of El Salvador
7) Compulsory military service according to age and other qualifications
8) White, crystalline salt, Na_2SO_4
9) National Football League team in the state of Washington
10) Island where it is believed Christopher Columbus first landed

Answers:

1) Solar system
2) Sargasso Sea
3) Sargent Shriver
4) Seven seas
5) Sirhan Sirhan
6) San Salvador
7) Selective Service
8) Sodium sulfate
9) Seattle Seahawks
10) San Salvador

NOBEL PRIZES

Identify each of the following concerning Nobel Prizes.

1) U.S. President who was the first American to win the peace prize
2) First winner in physics
3) First woman to win twice
4) Nation winning most in literature
5) First American to win in literature
6) Winner of 2 Nobel Prizes, in 1954 for chemistry and in 1962 for peace
7) First British person to win in literature
8) Second Russian to win in literature
9) Newest category added
10) Nation that has won the most peace prizes

Answers:

1) Theodore Roosevelt
2) Wilhelm Conrad Roentgen
3) Marie Curie
4) France
5) Sinclair Lewis
6) Linus Pauling
7) Rudyard Kipling
8) Boris Pasternak (Ivan Bunin was first)
9) Economics
10) U.S.

THE WORD *MOTHER*

Identify each of the following by giving an answer that includes the word *mother*.

1) Woman who won the Nobel Peace prize in 1979 for her work with the poor in India
2) Woman in charge of female religious community
3) Nursery rhyme character who went to get her poor dog a bone
4) Personification of natural world
5) Tales written by Frenchman Charles Perrault
6) Rich vein of ore
7) One's native language
8) Words completing the proverb, "Necessity is the ________"
9) Personification of the planet on which we live
10) Dorm mom

Answers:

1) Mother Teresa
2) Mother Superior
3) Mother Hubbard (or Old Mother Hubbard)
4) Mother Nature
5) *Tales of Mother Goose*
6) Mother lode
7) Mother tongue
8) Mother of invention
9) Mother Earth
10) Housemother

MULTIPLE CHOICE VOCABULARY

Choose the correct answer for each of the following concerning vocabulary.

1) Is a *martinet* considered to be a strict disciplinarian, a philosopher, a disbeliever in God, or a thief?
2) Which of the following does not end in *-able*: irritable, irascible, imperturbable, or insatiable?
3) Does *perfunctory* mean cautious, prompt, thorough, or superficial?
4) If you are being *ostracized*, are you being welcomed, banned, robbed, or hired?
5) Does *disparity* mean sadness, excitement, difference, or dishonesty?
6) If a person is *taciturn*, is he aggressive, quiet, talkative, or sleepy?
7) If a person is *sagacious*, is he shrewd, foolish, distracted, or naive?
8) If a person is *adamant*, is he unemotional, exhausted, first chronologically, or inflexible?
9) Of *parsley, sage, rosemary, or thyme*, which one also designates a wise man?
10) If a person is *corpulent*, is he tired, rich, fat, or irritable?

Answers:

1) Strict disciplinarian
2) Irascible
3) Superficial
4) Banned
5) Difference
6) Quiet
7) Shrewd
8) Inflexible
9) Sage
10) Fat

THE LETTER *P*

Identify each of the following by giving an answer beginning with the letter *P*.

1) Word from Greek philosophy to describe a relationship free from sensual desire
2) Mythical bird that renewed itself from its ashes
3) Author of *The Tale of Peter Rabbit*
4) Medal awarded to a member of the U.S. armed forces wounded in action
5) Base whose formula is KOH
6) Mountain chain, the "Backbone of England," covering half the length of England
7) Musician with the magic pipe who led its children away
8) Former home of Italian kings and currently a museum in Florence, Italy
9) First woman appointed to the Cabinet, the Secretary of Labor under President Franklin D. Roosevelt
10) Acid whose formula is $HClO_4$

Answers:

1) Platonic
2) Phoenix
3) (Beatrix) Potter
4) Purple Heart
5) Potassium hydroxide
6) Pennines (Pennine Chain)
7) Pied Piper of Hamelin (Hameln; accept Pied Piper)
8) Pitti Palace
9) (Frances) Perkins
10) Perchloric acid

HISTORY

Identify each of the following concerning history.

1) Former East European country whose city of Titograd was named after the leader who served from 1945 until 1980
2) Longest reigning British monarch, who served from 1837 to 1901
3) Year Germany invaded Poland on September 1 to start World War II
4) First English child born in the New World
5) General who cabled President Lincoln, "Atlanta is ours and fairly won"
6) U.S. President who died in San Francisco on August 2, 1923
7) First U.S. President to be assassinated in the 20th century
8) Country in which Pierre Trudeau replaced Lester Pearson as prime minister in 1968
9) U.S. state whose name identifies the battleship blown up in Havana in 1898
10) Pepin the Short's eldest son who in 774 assumed the iron crown of Lombardy

Answers:

1) Yugoslavia
2) Queen Victoria
3) 1939
4) Virginia Dare
5) General William Sherman
6) Warren Harding
7) William McKinley
8) Canada
9) *Maine*
10) Charlemagne (accept Charles I or Charles the Great)

MYTHOLOGY

Identify each of the following concerning mythology.

1) God of the dead in Greek mythology, called Pluto in Roman mythology
2) Architect of the Labyrinth in which the half-man, half-bull lived
3) Half-man, half-bull that lived in the Cretan Labyrinth
4) Number of Olympians in Greek mythology
5) Greek island that was the home of Ulysses
6) Winner of the golden apple inscribed "To the Fairest" in the beauty contest
7) Tragic king who killed his father and married his mother
8) Name for Medusa and her 2 hideous sisters
9) City-state ruled by Oedipus
10) Nymph on whose island Odysseus spent 7 years

Answers:

1) Hades
2) Daedalus
3) Minotaur
4) 12
5) Ithaca
6) Aphrodite
7) Oedipus
8) Gorgons
9) Thebes
10) Calypso

ANSWERS THAT INCLUDE DOUBLE LETTERS

Identify each of the following with an answer that includes a doubling of the given letter.

1) M - U.N. secretary-general awarded the Nobel Peace Prize posthumously in 1961
2) N - English poet laureate who wrote *In Memoriam* and *Idylls of the King*
3) C - African country whose capital is Rabat
4) G - Southern term for Northerners who travelled south during Reconstruction
5) A - Major league player with 755 career home runs
6) F - Brooding hero of Emily Brontë's *Wuthering Heights*
7) D - Father of American Rocketry
8) L - Conic section with an eccentricity value between 0 and 1
9) E - Term for the side of a mountain that faces away from the wind
10) B - Adjective for the phase of the moon when it is more than half full but less than full

Answers:

1) (Dag) Hammarskjöld
2) (Alfred, Lord) Tennyson
3) Morocco
4) Carpetbagger
5) (Hank) Aaron
6) Heathcliff
7) (Robert) Goddard
8) Ellipse
9) Leeward (side)
10) Gibbous

FINE ARTS

Identify each of the following concerning fine arts.

1) Nickname for Mozart's Symphony No. 41 in C that also identifies the supreme deity in Roman mythology
2) Gothic cathedral on Paris's Ile de la Cité
3) America's first great urban park designed for New York City by Frederick Law Olmsted
4) German composer who become totally deaf and was unable to hear his *Ninth Symphony*
5) 16th century Italian artist who painted the ceiling of the Sistine Chapel
6) Musical instrument that derives its name from a shortened form of the Italian for "soft and loud"
7) French term for a thin board on which an artist mixes pigments
8) Italian phrase for "without musical accompaniment"
9) Painting by Thomas Gainsborough to prove that a blue painting need not be dull
10) Term meaning "eighth part" that designates a musical interval, sometimes from middle C to the C above it

Answers:

1) Jupiter
2) Cathedral of Notre Dame (accept Notre Dame)
3) Central Park
4) Ludwig van Beethoven
5) Michelangelo
6) Piano (from *pianoforte*)
7) Palette
8) *A cappella*
9) *The Blue Boy*
10) Octave

WOMEN IN WORLD POLITICS

Identify each of the following women in world politics.

1) Shakespeare's "lass unparalleled" who took the Egyptian throne, in 51 B.C.
2) Europe's first woman prime minister, nicknamed "The Iron Lady"
3) English monarch who said, "I have the heart and stomach of a king"
4) Monarch who helped bring about unification of Spain in 15th century
5) Milwaukee woman who served as Israel's prime minister from 1969-1974
6) Indian prime minister 1966-1977 and from 1980 until assassinated in 1984
7) "Enlightened despot" who ruled Russia for 34 years in 18th century
8) English monarch who celebrated her Diamond Jubilee in 1897
9) First "Presidenta" of Argentina, wife of the general elected president in 1946
10) First woman pharaoh to rule Egypt, from 1503 to 1482 B.C.

Answers:

1) Cleopatra
2) Margaret Thatcher
3) Queen Elizabeth I
4) Queen Isabella
5) Golda Meir
6) Indira Gandhi
7) Catherine the Great (Catherine II)
8) Queen Victoria
9) Eva Perón
10) Hatshepsut

LITERATURE

Identify each of the following concerning literature.

1) First and last names of the educator who compiled the earliest American dictionaries
2) American humorist and cartoonist who created the character Walter Mitty
3) Country in which Ernest Hemingway's *The Old Man and the Sea* is set
4) Shakespearean character who says, "Good night, good night! parting is such sweet sorrow / That I shall say good night till it be morrow"
5) American winner of the 1993 Nobel Prize for literature
6) English poet known for his dramatic monologues such as "My Last Duchess"
7) American poet whose "Annabel Lee" is an idealized account of his wife, Virginia Clemm
8) Chief villain in Harriet Beecher Stowe's *Uncle Tom's Cabin*
9) American writer better known by his initials than by his name, Edward Estlin
10) Sorceress who in many versions of the King Arthur legend plots against him

Answers:

1) Noah Webster
2) James Thurber
3) Cuba
4) Juliet (in *Romeo and Juliet*)
5) Toni Morrison
6) Robert Browning
7) Edgar Allan Poe
8) Simon Legree
9) E.E. Cummings (or e.e. cummings)
10) Morgan le Fay

THE LETTER *R*

Identify each of the following by giving an answer beginning with the letter *R*.

1) Shift in the light of stars toward the longer wavelength end of the spectrum
2) Popular name for the narrow zone of volcanoes encircling the Pacific basin
3) Capital of Saskatchewan
4) European capital in which the Trevi Fountain is located
5) Disease known as German measles
6) Shorter and thicker bone of the 2 bones of the forearm
7) Author of *The Yearling*
8) Italian composer of the opera *William Tell*
9) U.S. state capital, home of the Research Triangle complex and President Andrew Johnson's birthplace
10) Muslim organization equivalent to the Red Cross

Answers:

1) Red shift
2) Ring of Fire
3) Regina
4) Rome
5) Rubella
6) Radius
7) (Marjorie Kinnan) Rawlings
8) (Gioacchino Antonio) Rossini
9) Raleigh
10) Red Crescent

DIGESTIVE SYSTEM

Identify each of the following concerning the digestive system.

1) Last part of the small intestine, between the jejunum and the large intestine
2) Inflammation of the intestines
3) Inflammation of the stomach
4) Body's largest gland, that aids digestion by producing bile
5) First process in the digestion of food, one involving chewing or breaking down the food
6) Large gland behind the stomach that secretes insulin to help regulate blood sugar levels
7) Inflammation of the pouches or sacs that have protruded through the walls of the colon
8) Enlarged veins inside or outside the anal canal
9) Degenerative disease of the liver, usually caused by chronic alcoholism
10) Tube that carries on most of the digestive process

Answers:

1) Ileum
2) Enteritis
3) Gastritis
4) Liver
5) Mastication
6) Pancreas
7) Diverticulitis
8) Hemorrhoids
9) Cirrhosis
10) Small intestine (accept duodenum)

HISTORY

Identify each of the following concerning history.

1) Leader who said in a speech in November 1914, "The maxim of the British people is 'Business as usual'"
2) Country in whose northern part the Boxer Rebellion took place in 1899-1900
3) U.S. state in which Cecil Calvert and the Calvert family served as the proprietors
4) French explorer who founded the city of Quebec
5) China's revolutionary Communist leader who led the famous "Long March" beginning in 1934
6) War fought between the 2 English royal houses, the House of York and the House of Lancaster
7) 2 of the 3 Baltic states that were forcibly annexed by the USSR in 1940
8) King of Great Britain and Ireland when Wellington won at Waterloo in 1815
9) Caribbean country that was the subject of the Platt Amendment in 1901
10) One of the Catherines besides Catherine of Aragón who became wives of Henry VIII

Answers:

1) Winston Churchill
2) China
3) Maryland
4) Samuel de Champlain
5) Mao Tse-tung (or Mao Zedong)
6) War of the Roses
7) Estonia, Latvia, and Lithuania
8) George III (he was in office from 1760 to 1820)
9) Cuba
10) Catherine Howard or Catherine Parr

AFRICAN-AMERICAN HISTORY

Identify each of the following concerning African-American history.

1) African country that was the destination of the 86 freed African-American emigrants who arrived at Monrovia in 1822
2) First African-American president of major league baseball's National League, so named in 1989
3) First African-American woman orator to speak against slavery, born Isabella Baumfree
4) Harlem Renaissance poet who wrote "I, Too, Sing America" in *The Weary Blues*
5) First African-American chairman of the Democratic National Committee, elected in 1989
6) First president of the Southern Leadership Conference
7) Orator and antislavery leader born Frederick Augustus Washington Bailey in Maryland
8) First African-American to win an Oscar for a starring role, in 1963 for *Lilies of the Field*
9) U.S. Representative from Texas (1973-79) who was the first African-American U.S. Congresswoman from Texas
10) Author of the novel *The Sport of the Gods* who first acquired fame for his verses in dialect

Answers:

1) Liberia
2) Bill White
3) Sojourner Truth
4) Langston Hughes
5) Ronald H. Brown
6) Martin L. King Jr. (later the Southern Christian Leadership Conference)
7) Frederick Douglass
8) Sidney Poitier
9) Barbara Jordan
10) Paul Laurence Dunbar

WORDS INCLUDING THE LETTERS *AZ*

Identify each of the following by giving an answer including the letters *az*.

1) Mythical female warriors
2) Indians conquered by Cortés
3) Man Jesus raised from dead
4) Abbreviation of the AIDS drug azidothymidine
5) Largest South American country
6) Explorer who discovered New York harbor
7) German fascist party
8) Philippine President Aquino's first name
9) Yellow sapphire
10) Cardinal under Louis XIV

Answers:

1) Amazons
2) Aztecs
3) Lazarus
4) AZT
5) Brazil
6) (Giovanni da) Verrazano
7) Nazi
8) Corazon
9) Topaz
10) (Jules) Mazarin

U.S. HISTORY

Identify each of the following concerning U.S. history.

1) President who in 1823 warned European powers to stay out of the Americas
2) Famous aviator known as "The Lone Eagle"
3) General remembered for saying, "I shall return"
4) War ended by the Treaty of Ghent
5) First President to die in office, in 1841
6) President paralyzed by a stroke in 1919
7) First U.S. Vice President to become President
8) American shot down in a U-2 plane in 1960 and captured by the Soviets
9) Nebraskan who made his "Cross of Gold" speech in 1896
10) Alabama city in which a bus boycott was begun in December 1955

Answers:

1) James Monroe (Monroe Doctrine)
2) Charles Lindbergh
3) Douglas MacArthur
4) War of 1812
5) William Henry Harrison
6) Woodrow Wilson
7) John Adams
8) Francis Gary Powers
9) William Jennings Bryan
10) Montgomery

POTPOURRI

Identify each of the following.

1) Symbol shaped like the moon in its first or last quarter that appears on the flags of Mauritania and Turkey
2) Planet with the most known satellites
3) War during which Francis Scott Key wrote "The Star-Spangled Banner"
4) World's longest river
5) Name of Paul Bunyan's gigantic blue ox
6) Big Ten university whose teams are nicknamed the "Nittany Lions"
7) Two middle names of President George Bush
8) U.S. state where the Winter Olympic Games were held in Lake Placid in 1932 and 1980
9) Geologic term for the narrow strip of land that connects North and South America
10) U.S. capital city in whose harbor the U.S.S. *Constitution* is located

Answers:

1) Crescent
2) Saturn
3) War of 1812
4) Nile River
5) Babe
6) Penn State University
7) Herbert Walker
8) New York
9) Isthmus
10) Boston

THE LETTER *S*

Identify each of the following by giving an answer beginning with the letter *S*.

1) U.S. capital city originally named "The Royal City of the Holy Faith of Saint Francis of Assisi"
2) Austrian composer known for his *lieder*, or songs
3) Artificial waterway joining the Mediterranean and Red seas
4) Killing of one's self
5) Slender stalk extending from the base of the female reproductive organ of a flower
6) Greek author of *Antigone* and *Oedipus at Colonus*
7) Charles Lindbergh's Ryan monoplane for 1927 flight
8) Straight line that intersects a circle at 2 points
9) Chemical symbol for antimony
10) System of heavy fortifications Hitler built to face the French line

Answers:

1) Santa Fe
2) (Franz) Schubert
3) Suez Canal
4) Suicide
5) Style
6) Sophocles
7) *Spirit of St. Louis*
8) Secant
9) Sb
10) Siegfried Line

MYTHOLOGY

Identify each of the following concerning mythology.

1) Daughter of Priam who repeatedly warned her countrymen not to take the Trojan Horse inside the walls of Troy
2) Patron goddess of Athens who was also the goddess of warfare and wisdom
3) Fruit the Greek goddess of Discord threw into a banquet of gods and goddesses
4) Term that designates the "mythological food of the gods"
5) Winged horse for whom the northern constellation between Cygnus, Pisces, and Aquarius is named
6) Mythological Muse of eloquence and epic poetry
7) Person who ferried the dead across the River Styx
8) Handsome young man loved by Aphrodite, who was killed by a boar
9) Muse of history
10) Wife of Hector

Answers:

1) Cassandra
2) Athena (or Pallas Athena)
3) Apple (also called the Apple of Discord)
4) Ambrosia
5) Pegasus
6) Calliope
7) Charon
8) Adonis
9) Clio
10) Andromache

GEOGRAPHY

Identify each of the following concerning geography.

1) City, called Firenze in Italian, where the Medicis exerted a powerful influence from the early 1400s until 1737
2) Alaskan peak that is the highest in North America
3) River that flows past the Houses of Parliament and the Tower of London
4) Himalayan peak that is the world's highest
5) Senator known as "The Great Compromiser," for whom many counties in the U.S. are named
6) Sea on which Venice, Italy, is situated
7) City that serves as the seat of government in The Netherlands
8) U.S.'s oldest city, in Florida
9) France's chief commercial waterway, which flows through Paris and into the English Channel
10) Swedish capital, where all Nobel Prizes except for the Nobel Peace Prize are awarded

Answers:

1) Florence
2) Mount McKinley
3) Thames
4) Mount Everest (called Sagarmatha in Nepali, Qomolangma Feng in Chinese, and Chomolungma in Tibetan)
5) Clay (after Henry Clay)
6) Adriatic Sea
7) The Hague
8) St. Augustine
9) Seine River
10) Stockholm

P-A-R FOR THE COURSE

Identify each of the following by giving an answer beginning with the letters *P-A-R*.

1) Degenerative disease of later life characterized by tremors, shuffling walk, and slow speech
2) South American country whose capital is Asunción
3) What is found in a pear tree in the song "Twelve Days of Christmas"
4) Act of murdering one's parent
5) Doric temple of Athena built on the Acropolis in Athens
6) Name of brain lobe between frontal and occipital lobes
7) John Milton's epic poem
8) American poet who wrote, "Men seldom make passes / At girls who wear glasses."
9) Greek mountain sacred to Apollo and the Muses in ancient times
10) South American capital whose country is Surinam(e)

Answers:

1) Parkinson's Disease (Parkinsonism)
2) Paraguay
3) Partridge
4) Parricide
5) Parthenon
6) Parietal lobe
7) *Paradise Lost* (or *Paradise Regained*)
8) (Dorothy) Parker
9) Parnassus
10) Paramaribo

STRAITS

Identify each of the following concerning straits.

1) Mythological lovers who drowned in the Dardanelles, he in a storm and she because of his death
2) Strait connecting the Atlantic Ocean with the Mediterranean Sea
3) U.S. state and area of Russia separated by the Bering Strait
4) Strait at South American extremity between the mainland and the Tierra del Fuego Archipelago
5) Two continents separated by the Drake Passage, the strait between Cape Horn and the South Shetland Islands
6) Strait that connects the Sea of Marmara and Black Sea
7) Michigan city that derives its name from the French for "strait"
8) Two Great Lakes connected by the Straits of Mackinac
9) Mythological rock and whirlpool located on the Strait of Messina
10) Southwest Pacific Ocean country divided into 2 parts by the Cook Strait

Answers:

1) Hero and Leander
2) Strait of Gibraltar
3) Alaska and Siberia
4) Strait of Magellan
5) South America and Antarctica
6) Bosporous Strait
7) Detroit
8) Lake Michigan and Lake Huron
9) Scylla and Charybdis
10) New Zealand

VOCABULARY

Give the word or phrase defined by each of the following.

1) Leave of absence traditionally granted at 7-year intervals to college teachers
2) French phrase for a "dead-end street" or "blind alley"
3) Colorful phrase for both a valuable asset and a stock of high investment quality
4) Word derived from Greek mythology for "to tease" or "tempt"
5) General psychological term to designate a "loss of memory"
6) Word meaning "before the war" that describes houses built prior to the U.S. Civil War
7) Word for a long speech used to obstruct the passage of a bill, especially in the U.S. Senate
8) Word for a more pleasant term used in place of one considered harsh or offensive
9) Latin phrase for "seize the day," a motif used in the film *Dead Poets Society*
10) Word for "a person who suffers persecution for his faith"

Answers:

1) Sabbatical
2) Cul-de-sac
3) Blue chip
4) Tantalize (from Tantalus)
5) Amnesia
6) Antebellum
7) Filibuster
8) Euphemism
9) *Carpe diem*
10) Martyr

LITERATURE

Identify each of the following concerning literature.

1) American poet who wrote, "Poems are made by fools like me, / But only God can make a tree"
2) First poet to be honored with burial in Westminster Abbey
3) Animal into which Hans Christian Andersen's Ugly Duckling turns
4) Author who tells of the migration of Oklahoma sharecroppers to California in *The Grapes of Wrath*
5) British author born Eric Arthur Blair
6) Novel in which Santiago dreams about lions playing on the beach
7) New England poet who wrote over 1700 poems but had only 7 published during her lifetime
8) Language in which the story of Pinocchio was originally written
9) Surname of Edwin Arlington Robinson's alcoholic failure, Miniver ________
10) Day and year Paul Revere made his famous ride according to Longfellow's "Paul Revere's Ride"

Answers:

1) Joyce Kilmer (in "Trees")
2) Geoffrey Chaucer
3) Swan
4) John Steinbeck
5) George Orwell
6) *The Old Man and the Sea* (by Ernest Hemingway)
7) Emily Dickinson
8) Italian (by Carlo Collodi; born Carlo Lorenzini)
9) Cheevy
10) "on the eighteenth of April, in Seventy-five"

THE LETTER *T*

Identify each of the following by giving an answer beginning with the letter *T*.

1) Element named for the mythological king condemned to stand in water and remain eternally thirsty
2) Name for the more than 1,500 densely wooded islands in the St. Lawrence River
3) Larger of the 2 bones located between the knee and the ankle
4) U.S. state capital that is the site of the Menninger Foundation, a noted psychiatric center
5) Robert Louis Stevenson book in which Captain Flint is a character
6) 1811 battle at which William Henry Harrison's forces defeated the Prophet, Tecumseh's brother
7) Set of three related plays or novels
8) Temperature and pressure at which all three phases of a substance are in equilibrium
9) British author of "Charge of the Light Brigade"
10) Framework of sticks American Indians used as a sled

Answers:

1) Tantalum
2) Thousand Islands
3) Tibia
4) Topeka
5) *Treasure Island*
6) Tippecanoe
7) Trilogy
8) Triple-Point
9) (Alfred, Lord) Tennyson
10) Travois(e)

LUNGS AND BREATHING

Identify each of the following terms concerning lungs and breathing.

1) Disease first identified in 1976 when an epidemic struck an American Legion convention in a Philadelphia hotel
2) Sudden involuntary contraction causing a blocking of the bronchial tubes during an asthma attack
3) Disabling lung disease that affects coal miners
4) Disabling lung disease that affects workers in cotton textile mills
5) More technical term for the chest in the human body
6) Term for releasing air out of the lungs as the diaphragm and rib muscles relax
7) Term for taking air into the lungs through the windpipe
8) Hereditary disease that causes excessive thick mucous resulting in chronic respiratory infections
9) Disease for which an iron lung was the chief device used during the epidemic of the 1950s
10) Thick mucus that gathers in the lungs during an asthma attack

Answers:

1) Legionnaires' disease
2) Spasm
3) Black lung (accept coal worker's pneumoconiosis)
4) Brown lung (accept byssinosis)
5) Thorax
6) Expiration (or exhalation)
7) Inspiration (or inhalation)
8) Cystic fibrosis (of the pancreas)
9) Polio (or poliomyelitis)
10) Phlegm

FAMOUS PEOPLE WITH THE SAME SURNAMES

Identify the surname shared by all 3 famous people in following groups.

1) Charles Francis, Samuel, John Quincy
2) Melville Weston, Margaret, R. Buckminster
3) Michael, Andrew, Jesse
4) De Witt, William, Hillary
5) Richard, Increase, Cotton
6) Anne, Emily, Charlotte
7) Samuel, Andrew, Lyndon
8) Alfred E., Jedediah Strong, Margaret Chase
9) John Davison, Winthrop, Nelson
10) Joseph, Shirley Temple, Hugo Lafayette

Answers:

1) Adams
2) Fuller
3) Jackson
4) Clinton
5) Mather
6) Brontë
7) Johnson
8) Smith
9) Rockefeller
10) Black

U.S. PRESIDENTIAL ELECTION YEARS

Identify each of the following presidential election years from the given information.

1) Democrats Pierce and King defeated Whigs Scott and Graham
2) Democrats Polk and Dallas defeated Whigs Clay and Frelinghuysen
3) Republicans Grant and Colfax defeated Democrats Seymour and Blair
4) Democrats Jackson and Calhoun defeated National Republicans Adams and Rush
5) Democrats Buchanan and Breckinridge defeated Republicans Frémont and Dayton
6) Democrats Cleveland and Hendricks defeated Republicans Blaine and Logan
7) Democrats Van Buren and Johnson defeated Whigs Harrison and Granger
8) Democrats Jackson and Van Buren defeated National Republicans Clay and Sergeant
9) Republicans Harrison and Morton defeated Democrats Cleveland and Thurman
10) Republicans Garfield and Arthur defeated Democrats Hancock and English

Answers:

1) 1852
2) 1844
3) 1868
4) 1828
5) 1856
6) 1884
7) 1836
8) 1832
9) 1888
10) 1880

PHILOSOPHERS

Name each of the following philosophers based on the brief biographical description.

1) Author who in *The Social Contract* views the government as the expression of the will of the people
2) Author who in *Leviathan* purports that man is selfish by nature
3) German philosopher who wrote such works as *Thus Spake Zarathustra* and *Beyond Good and Evil*
4) Frenchman who set forth in *The Spirit of Laws* the theory of separation of powers that influenced the writing of the U.S. Constitution
5) Materialist thinker of the French Enlightenment and originator of the *Encyclopédie*
6) Philosopher who established the philosophical school called "The Lyceum"
7) Scottish thinker who was a forerunner of empiricism and author of *A Treatise of Human Nature and An Enquiry Concerning Human Understanding*
8) American educator who attacked the belief that knowledge was passive and helped to lead the movement of progressive education
9) German philosopher who studied history and metaphysics through a trio of stages, called thesis, antithesis, and synthesis
10) 17th-century German who influenced Voltaire with his belief that this is the best of all possible worlds

Answers:

1) Jean Jacques Rousseau
2) Thomas Hobbes
3) Friedrich Wilhelm Nietzsche
4) Baron de Montesquieu
5) Denis Diderot (or Jean d'Alembert)
6) Aristotle
7) David Hume
8) John Dewey
9) Georg W.F. Hegel
10) Gottfried Wilhelm Leibniz

ALFRED, LORD TENNYSON

Identify each of the following concerning Alfred, Lord Tennyson.

1) Poem which includes the line, "My strength is as the strength of ten, / Because my heart is pure."
2) Post he held from 1850 to 1892
3) His intimate friend who died suddenly and about whom he wrote an elegy
4) Elegy written in memory of his intimate friend who died suddenly
5) Site in Westminster Abbey where he was buried
6) Patriotic ode written on the death of the person who defeated Napoleon at Waterloo
7) Poem inspired by an incident in the Crimean War
8) Narrative poem concerning the effect of the materialistic spirit on a sensitive young lover
9) Series of 12 narrative poems about King Arthur and his court
10) Poem based on the seaside mansion of his youth

Answers:

1) "Sir Galahad"
2) Poet Laureate
3) Arthur Henry Hallam
4) *In Memoriam*
5) Poets' Corner
6) "Ode on the Death of the Duke of Wellington"
7) "The Charge of the Light Brigade" (accept "The Charge of the Heavy Brigade")
8) *Maud*
9) *Idylls of the King*
10) *Locksley Hall*

MIDDLE

Identify each of the following beginning with the word *middle*.

1) Musical note on the first line below the treble staff and the first above the bass staff
2) Period of European history from A.D. 476 to about 1450
3) Part of the body where the hammer, anvil, and stirrup are located
4) Area from Afghanistan to Libya, especially Israel, Jordan, and Lebanon
5) Chinese name for its Chinese Empire, thought to be the center of the world
6) Intermediary agent between two parties
7) Boxer more than 155 pounds but less than 160 pounds
8) George Eliot's or Mary Ann Evans' novel subtitled *A Study of Provincial Life*
9) Avoiding extremes, especially of the political left and right
10) Where the Hobbits live in J.R.R. Tolkien's fantasies

Answers:

1) Middle C
2) Middle Ages
3) Middle ear
4) Middle East
5) Middle Kingdom
6) Middleman
7) Middleweight
8) *Middlemarch*
9) Middle of the road
10) Middle Earth

LITERARY MOVEMENTS

Identify each of the following concerning literary groups or movements.

1) 20th century school of drama focusing on the meaninglessness of life, exemplified by playwrights Beckett and Genet
2) Group of 17th century poets, including John Donne, who developed elaborate conceits in their verse
3) Form of romanticism based on the belief that individuals can learn truths that exceed the senses, espoused by Emerson and Thoreau
4) Literary movement founded by poet André Breton in 1924 in an effort to free the mind from logic and reason
5) School represented by Tolstoy and Dostoevski, who attempted to exemplify things as they really are
6) 19th century movement represented by the works of Wordsworth, Byron, and Shelley
7) Ezra Pound, Amy Lowell, and other poets who in the years prior to WWI focused on precise, definite pictures in their poetry
8) Renaissance movement focusing on the exalting of mankind, as exemplified by the writings of Erasmus, Boccaccio, and Sir Thomas More
9) 19th-20th century movement based on belief that external and internal forces control men, exemplified by Zola and Stephen Crane
10) Poets such as Mallarmé, Baudelaire, and Verlaine who rebelled against the Parnassians and traditional French poetry

Answers:

1) Theatre of the Absurd
2) Metaphysical poets
3) Transcendentalism
4) Surrealism
5) Realism
6) Romanticism
7) Imagists
8) Humanism
9) Naturalism
10) Symbolists

SCIENCE

Identify each of the following concerning science.

1) Part of the brain that controls the coordination of the muscles and consists of a middle lobe and 2 lateral lobes
2) SI unit of force named after a British scientist and equal to 1 kilogram meter per second squared
3) Parasitic disease of tropical and subtropical areas transmitted by the bite of the female *Anopheles* mosquito
4) Latin term meaning "in glass" used to designate an artificial environment, such as a test tube
5) Genus of one-celled flagellates, classified as algae, that live in fresh water and can form a green scum in small ponds
6) Circumference of the earth at the equator: about 15,000, 20,000, 25,000, or 30,000 miles
7) Word describing the orbit of a satellite that is maintaining its position over the same spot on the earth
8) Word defined as "two or more atoms with the same atomic number but with different atomic weights"
9) Unit of thermodynamic temperature indicated by the letter *K*
10) Term derived from the Greek for "to shake" for the shock waves produced by an earthquake or by a manmade explosion

Answers:

1) Cerebellum
2) Newton
3) Malaria (paludism or swamp fever)
4) *In vitro*
5) Euglena
6) 25,000 miles
7) Geosynchronous (accept geostationary)
8) Isotopes
9) Kelvin
10) Seismic waves

MATH FEATURING PLANES

Identify each of the following concerning planes.

1) Name given to 2 or more distinct circles that lie in the same plane and have the same center
2) Number of lines determined by 5 different points in a plane if no 3 points are collinear
3) Locus of points in a given plane 10 cm from a given line in that plane
4) Word used to describe 2 circles that lie in the same plane and have exactly one point in common
5) Of area, angle measure, or distance, the one that is invariant under a dilation in a plane
6) Conic section obtained when a plane intersects a right circular cone perpendicular to its axis
7) Of regular hexagon, scalene triangle, and regular pentagon, the one that cannot be used to tesselate a plane
8) Number of planes of symmetry in a cube
9) Angle formed by two half-planes with a common edge
10) Type of planar trapezoid with one line of symmetry

Answers:

1) Concentric circles
2) 10
3) 2 lines (the 2 lines are parallel to the given line)
4) Tangent
5) Angle measure
6) Circle
7) Regular pentagon
8) 9
9) Dihedral (angle)
10) Isosceles

WORDS INCLUDING THE LETTERS *AZ*

Identify each of the following by giving an answer including the letters *az*.

1) Swing music
2) To demolish a building
3) Black Hills Indian sculpture
4) To mark a trail
5) Egyptian-Israeli disputed area
6) One of the Magi
7) Sky blue
8) "New Colossus" poet
9) African country
10) Bolivian capital

Answers:

1) Jazz
2) Raze
3) Crazy Horse
4) Blaze
5) Gaza (Strip)
6) Balthazar
7) Azure
8) (Emma) Lazarus
9) Swaziland
10) La Paz

WORDS BEGINNING WITH *M-I-S*

Identify the following, each of which begins with the letters *mis*.

1) 1820 act in which slavery was prohibited in the Louisiana Purchase north of latitude 36 degrees 30 minutes North
2) Hatred of mankind
3) Ridge in northwest Georgia and southeast Tennessee where an 1863 Civil War battle was fought
4) 1888 play by August Strindberg
5) Made up of a variety of parts
6) Prayer book
7) Mismanagement, or failure to attain desired end
8) Hatred of women
9) Villain; depraved person
10) Minor legal infraction

Answers:

1) Missouri Compromise (slavery prohibited except in Missouri)
2) Misanthropy
3) Missionary Ridge
4) *Miss Julie*
5) Miscellaneous
6) Missal
7) Miscarriage (as in "miscarriage of justice")
8) Misogyny
9) Miscreant
10) Misdemeanor

LOGIC AND REASONING

Identify the following terms associated with logic and reasoning.

1) Statement proposed for consideration, especially one to be discussed and proved
2) Proposition from which a conclusion will be drawn
3) Form of reasoning consisting of a major premise, a minor premise, and a conclusion
4) Argument requiring a choice between 2 or more unfavorable solutions
5) Latin phrase for reasoning from a general law to a particular instance
6) An equally assertible and apparently contradictory proposition
7) Method of reasoning used by Georg Wilhelm Friedrich Hegel
8) Process of reasoning from particular to general
9) Reconciliation of opposites in Hegelian Dialectic
10) Process of reasoning in which conclusions are drawn from premises presented

Answers:

1) Thesis
2) Premise
3) Syllogism
4) Dilemma
5) A priori
6) Antithesis
7) Dialectic
8) Induction
9) Synthesis
10) Deduction

TREATIES

Identify each of the following concerning treaties.

1) Fractional part of the total vote represented by the 67 votes necessary for ratification of a treaty in the U.S. Senate
2) Treaty signed on February 11, 1929, by Benito Mussolini with the papacy
3) Belgian city where the treaty ending the War of 1812 was signed
4) U.S. treaty signed in 1794 with Great Britain by the Chief Justice
5) Treaty that ended World War I
6) 1819 treaty by which Spain ceded Florida to the U.S.
7) Full name for the organization established in a 1949 treaty for the defense of 12 Western nations
8) Full name of SEATO, an organization of 8 nations that signed a defense treaty in 1954
9) Treaty signed on February 10, 1763, to end the French and Indian War
10) Peace treaty for which Handel's *Royal Fireworks Music* was composed to celebrate the end of the War of Austrian Succession

Answers:

1) Two-thirds (assuming all senators are present)
2) Lateran Treaty
3) Ghent (Treaty of Ghent)
4) Jay's Treaty (Jay Treaty)
5) Treaty of Versailles
6) Adams-Onís Treaty (accept Transcontinental Treaty or Florida Purchase Treaty)
7) North Atlantic Treaty Organization (by the North Atlantic Treaty)
8) Southeast Asia Treaty Organization (the treaty was the Southeast Asia Collective Defense Treaty)
9) Treaty of Paris
10) Peace of Aix-la-Chapelle

JAPAN

Give the Japanese word for each of the following aspects of its culture.

1) Traditional art or technique of folding paper
2) Female trained as a professional entertainer and companion for men
3) Ceremonial suicide committed by ripping open the stomach with a dagger
4) Member of the hereditary feudal warrior caste
5) Large sea wave caused by an undersea volcanic eruption
6) Country's native religion
7) WWII pilot on a suicide mission
8) Member of the aboriginal population of northernmost Japan
9) Seaport on Honshu, south of Tokyo, whose name means "cross shore"
10) Code of the hereditary feudal warrior caste

Answers:

1) Origami
2) Geisha
3) Seppuku (accept hara-kiri or hari-kari)
4) Samurai
5) Tsunami (accept seismic sea wave)
6) Shinto
7) Kamikaze
8) Ainu
9) Yokohama
10) Bushido

JUDGES

Identify each of the following concerning judges.

1) U.S. President of the 1930s who tried to place additional judges on the Supreme Court
2) Term of office of Supreme Court and other federal court judges
3) New York State Supreme Court judge who disappeared forever in August 1930
4) Judge who presided over the Watergate hearings
5) Waltham, Massachusetts, university whose athletic teams are nicknamed the "Judges"
6) U.S. President whose first 2 nominees for the Supreme Court were rejected before his 3rd was accepted by the Senate in 1970
7) "Kenesaw Mountain" judge who was the first commissioner of professional baseball
8) Court located in The Hague in the Netherlands whose 15 judges are elected to 9-year-terms
9) Judge nicknamed the "Only Law West of the Pecos" and the "Texas Hanging Judge"
10) Judge who presided over the split of American Telephone and Telegraph into smaller divisions in 1982-1983

Answers:

1) Franklin Roosevelt
2) For life
3) Joseph Force Crater
4) John Sirica
5) Brandeis University (after Louis Dembitz Brandeis)
6) Richard Nixon
7) Kenesaw Mountain Landis
8) World Court (accept International Court of Justice)
9) Roy Bean
10) Harold Greene

TRAINS

Identify each of the following concerning trains.

1) Time a train will arrive at its destination 220 miles away if it leaves the station at 6:30 a.m. and averages 55 miles per hour on its trip
2) Name of the traditional last car on a train
3) Full name of C&O, a railroad whose logo is a sleeping cat
4) European train known as "The King of Trains" and "The Train of Kings"
5) U.S. President assassinated in a train station in Washington, D.C. in 1881
6) Train robber allegedly shot and killed in Missouri in 1882 by Robert Ford, who is known as the "dirty little coward"
7) Leo Tolstoy character who commits suicide by throwing herself under a train
8) American inventor of the air brake for railroad trains
9) Country whose fast trains are known as *TGV*'s
10) City in which The El (for elevated railway) runs along a rectangular "loop" 5 blocks wide and 7 blocks long

Answers:

1) 10:30 a.m.
2) Caboose
3) Chesapeake and Ohio (Railway Company)
4) The *Orient Express*
5) James Garfield
6) Jesse James
7) Anna Karenina
8) George Westinghouse
9) France [T.G.V. is *Train à (de) grande vitesse* or "very fast train"]
10) Chicago (this area is called the Loop)

AIRPLANES

Identify each of the following concerning airplanes.

1) Espionage plane in which Francis Gary Powers was shot down over the Soviet Union onMay 1, 1960
2) Only U.S. President who took the presidential oath on a plane
3) Lockheed plane named for the mythological daughter of Agamemnon and Clytemnestra that crashed in 1959 and 1960
4) Explosive sound that results when the cone-shaped shock wave caused by an airplane traveling at supersonic speed touches the ground
5) Swiss mathematician whose principle explains how airplane wings create the upward force called *lift*
6) Country whose passenger plane was shot down by Russians in 1983
7) Airline whose plane was exploded by bomb over Lockerbie, Scotland, in 1988
8) Country whose plane was accidentally shot down over the Persian Gulf in 1988 by the USS *Vincennes*
9) Small jet used as a company plane and named after its inventor
10) Seattle-based airplane manufacturer that is one of the world's largest

Answers:

1) U-2
2) Lyndon Johnson
3) *Electra*
4) Sonic boom
5) Bernoulli's
6) South Korea
7) Pan Am (Pan American)
8) Iran
9) Lear
10) Boeing

U.S. STREETS

Identify each of the following U.S. streets.

1) New York City street known as a financial district
2) New York City street associated with fashionable living and high society
3) New York City street whose name completes the song title, "Give My Regards to ________"
4) Most expensive green street in *Monopoly*
5) Los Angeles street known for its embedded stars bearing the names of celebrities
6) Washington, D.C., street on which the White House is located
7) San Francisco street called the "World's Most Crooked Street"
8) Beverly Hills street where the most expensive shops are located
9) New Orleans street known for its Dixieland jazz
10) Atlanta's most famous street and site of a Civil War battle

Answers:

1) Wall Street
2) Park Avenue
3) Broadway
4) Pennsylvania Avenue
5) Hollywood Boulevard
6) Pennsylvania Avenue
7) Lombard Street
8) Rodeo Drive
9) Bourbon Street
10) Peachtree Street

ALL ABOUT NUMBERS

Identify the following, each of which is associated with a number.

1) University whose president, Charles William Eliot, edited the "five-foot shelf of books"
2) Second Soviet space station whose name means "peace"
3) Austrian composer whose Eighth Symphony is also called the *Symphony of a Thousand*
4) Italian composer known for 4 concertos entitled *The Four Seasons*
5) Author of *Two Years Before the Mast*
6) Poet who penned "The Second Coming"
7) U.S. Vice President who said, "What this country needs is a good five-cent cigar"
8) Leader whose Red Shirts helped conquer the Kingdom of the Two Sicilies for the Kingdom of Italy in 1860
9) Fifth Chief Justice of the U.S. Supreme Court who served from 1836 to 1864 after succeeding John Marshall
10) Author of *The Fourth Protocol*

Answers:

1) Harvard University (the books are called the Harvard Classics)
2) *Mir*
3) Gustave Mahler
4) Antonio Vivaldi
5) Richard Henry Dana
6) William Butler Yeats
7) Thomas Marshall
8) Giuseppe Garibaldi
9) Roger Brooke Taney
10) Frederick Forsyth

FORMER U.S. STATE CAPITALS

Identify the state for which each of the following was formerly a capital.

1) Wheeling
2) Fort Leavenworth
3) Knoxville
4) Virginia City
5) Lexington
6) Tuscaloosa
7) Portland
8) Tucson
9) New Castle
10) Charleston

Answers:

1) West Virginia
2) Kansas
3) Tennessee
4) Montana
5) Kentucky
6) Alabama
7) Maine
8) Arizona
9) Delaware
10) South Carolina

U.S. STATES AND THEIR HIGHEST POINTS

Identify the U.S. state in which each of the following is the highest mountain.

1) Mt. Rainier
2) Guadalupe Peak
3) Mt. Washington
4) Mt. Mitchell
5) Mauna Kea
6) Mt. McKinley
7) Mt. Sunflower
8) Mt. Whitney
9) Mt. Katahdin
10) Mt. Marcy

Answers:

1) Washington
2) Texas
3) New Hampshire
4) North Carolina
5) Hawaii
6) Alaska
7) Kansas
8) California
9) Maine
10) New York

MATH TERMS

Identify each of the following terms used in math.

1) Number which can be expressed as x over y where x and y are integers and y does not equal zero
2) Segment joining the midpoints of the legs of a trapezoid
3) Geometrical solid having 8 triangular faces
4) Triangle with at least 2 congruent sides
5) System of locating planar points by pairs of numbers representing distances along two lines called axes
6) Two polyhedra having the same shape but not necessarily the same size
7) Name for the infinite sequence of numbers 1,1,2,3,5,8,13, and so on
8) In statistics, a measure of the relationship between two variables
9) Synonym for half-line
10) Identity element of addition

Answers:

1) Rational
2) Median (of a trapezoid)
3) Octahedron
4) Isosceles
5) Cartesian coordinates (in Plane Geometry)
6) Similar (Solids)
7) Fibonacci sequence
8) Correlation (coefficient)
9) Ray
10) Zero

WOMEN HONORED BY U.S. POSTAL STAMPS

Identify each of the following women honored by U.S. postal stamps.

1) "Moses of her People" who led slaves to safety on the "Underground Railroad"
2) 1st First Lady to attend the swearing-in of her husband, in 1809
3) Revolutionary heroine who carried water at a New Jersey battle
4) Aviatrix who disappeared over the Pacific in 1937
5) 1st woman presented the Congressional Medal of Honor, for heroic service during the Civil War
6) Daniel Parke Custis's widow who became the First Lady of the U.S.
7) Prison reform leader who headed the Union's nurses in the Civil War
8) Feminist who was first married woman to keep her maiden name
9) Feminist who with Lucretia Mott organized first women's rights convention in Seneca Falls, NY, in 1848
10) New York-born slave who became an anti-slavery orator, dubbed the "Libyan Sybil"

Answers:

1) Harriet Tubman
2) Dolley Madison
3) Molly Pitcher (Mary Ludwig or Mary Hays or Mary McCauley)
4) Amelia Earhart
5) Dr. Mary E. Walker
6) Martha Washington
7) Dorothea Dix
8) Lucy Stone
9) Elizabeth C. Stanton
10) Sojourner Truth

ENGLISH RULERS AND THEIR REIGNS

Identify the English ruler for each of the following periods.

1) 1399-1413
2) 1702-1714
3) 1422-1461 & 1470-1471
4) 1653-1658
5) 1558-1603
6) 1760-1820
7) 1483-1485
8) 1660-1685
9) 1603-1625
10) 1625-1649

Answers:

1) Henry IV
2) Anne
3) Henry VI
4) Oliver Cromwell
5) Elizabeth I
6) George III
7) Richard III
8) Charles II
9) James I
10) Charles I

BALLET COMPOSERS

Name the composer of the following famous ballets.

1) *Billy the Kid*
2) *The Nutcracker*
3) *Petruchka*
4) *Swan Lake*
5) *Giselle*
6) *The Three Cornered Hat*
7) *Rodeo*
8) *Fancy Free*
9) *Romeo and Juliet*
10) *The Seven Deadly Sins of the Petits Bourgeois*

Answers:

1) Aaron Copland
2) Peter Tchaikovsky
3) Igor Stravinsky
4) Peter Tchaikovsky
5) Adolphe Adam
6) Manuel de Falla
7) Aaron Copland
8) Leonard Bernstein
9) Sergei Prokofiev
10) Kurt Weill

GERMAN WORDS AND PHRASES

Give the English translation for each of the following German words and phrases.

1) *Guten Morgen*
2) *Guten Abend*
3) *Bitte*
4) *Danke schön*
5) *Wie geht's?*
6) *Guten Tag*
7) *Guten Nacht*
8) *Was ist das?*
9) *Was ist los?*
10) *Wissen Sie?*

Answers:

1) Good Morning
2) Good Evening
3) Please
4) Thank you very much
5) How are you?
6) Good afternoon
7) Good night
8) What's this?
9) What's the matter?
10) Do you know?

AFRICAN HISTORY

Answer the following questions concerning the history of Africa.

1) Group that invaded Egypt in 639 and completed the conquest of all northern Africa by 710
2) African country colonized by the American Colonization Society in the 1830s
3) National religion of Ethiopia as a result of the conversion of the inhabitants of the city of Auxum in mid-4th century
4) African people related by language who occupy almost all of southern Africa below the Congo river
5) Egyptian queen who helped to influence the religious reforms of her husband Akhenton
6) Thutmose II's wife who as queen brought peace to Egypt from 1489 B.C. until 1464 B.C.
7) Present-day country in which Mansa Musa and Modibo Keita ruled
8) African term for okra
9) Kingdom that occupied what is now central Ghana from the 17th century until the early 1900s
10) Kingdom south of Egypt that arose about 2000 B.C. and existed until about A.D. 350

Answers:

1) (Arab) Muslims
2) Liberia
3) Christianity or Coptic Church (Coptic Orthodox Church or Orthodox Church of Ethiopia)
4) Bantu
5) Nefertiti
6) Hatshepsut
7) Mali
8) Gumbo (nkruma)
9) Ashanti
10) Kush (Nubia, Ethiopia)

QUICK MATH

Answer each of the following quick math questions.

1) What name is given to two angles whose sides form two pairs of opposite rays?
2) What is the maximum number of points of intersection of two circles with different radii?
3) If the radius of a circle is doubled, by what factor is its area multiplied?
4) What is the conjugate of the complex number $a + bi$ (READ: a plus bee eye)?
5) What is the numerical value of 1 factorial divided by 0 factorial?
6) What is the numerical value of x to the 4th power if $x = -2$?
7) What type of geometric figure is represented by the equation $x^2 - 4x + y^2 = 6$
8) If $f(x)$ [READ: f of x] represents a function, what term is used to describe the set of all admissible values of x?
9) By what name is the graph of the equation $y = 3$ known?
10) By what name is the graph of the equation $x^2 + 2y^2 = 1$ known?

Answers:

1) Vertical (angles)
2) 2
3) 4
4) $a - bi$ (READ AS: a minus bee eye)
5) 1
6) 16 (do NOT accept –16)
7) Circle
8) Domain
9) Line (accept straight line or horizontal line; DO NOT ACCEPT vertical line)
10) Ellipse

PHILOSOPHIES

Name the philosophy centered on each of the following beliefs and advanced by the writers noted.

1) Natural laws and the scientific method alone can explain reality and truth
2) All existing institutions should be annihilated, as advocated by a movement in Russia in the 1860s
3) Reality exists independent of the mind
4) Things tend to be generally good, as asserted by Leibniz
5) God is visible everywhere, in nature, in objects, and in people
6) Things tend to be generally bad
7) There are many gods
8) Knowledge is intuitive, as asserted by Immanuel Kant
9) Practical actions and their results carry more weight than theory and tradition, as asserted by William James and John Dewey
10) Reason is the true basis of knowledge, as asserted by Georg W.F. Hegel

1) Naturalism
2) Nihilism
3) Objectivism
4) Optimism
5) Pantheism
6) Pessimism
7) Polytheism
8) Transcendentalism (transcendental philosophy)
9) Pragmatism
10) Rationalism

SHARES ITS NAME WITH

Identify each of the following that shares its name with something or someone else.

1) Name for Tchaikovsky symphony-fantasy Opus 18 that designates "a violent storm" and also identifies a Shakespearean play
2) Satellite of Neptune that shares its name with a mythological son of Poseidon and Amphitrite
3) Corrupt New York "Boss" and a wool fabric with a rough surface
4) Site of an ancient war fought in Turkey and a system of weights used for gold, silver, and precious gems
5) Russian city that shares its name with a popular Florida resort city and retirement center located on Tampa Bay
6) 1953 New Zealand conqueror of Mount Everest whose surname is the same as the first name of Bill Clinton's wife
7) Paul Bunyan's blue ox and slugger George Herman Ruth
8) U.S. President with the same surname as the governor who promoted the building of the Erie Canal
9) Dormant Asian volcano whose 4-letter name begins the surname of a President of Peru
10) Nickname of Natty Bumppo and John Charles Frémont

Answers:

1) Tempest
2) Triton
3) Tweed (William Marcy Tweed)
4) Troy
5) Saint Petersburg
6) (Sir Edmund Percival) Hillary
7) Babe
8) (Bill) Clinton (Governor De Witt Clinton)
9) (Mount) Fuji (Alberto Fujimori served as Peru's president)
10) "The Pathfinder"

FRENCH KINGS AND THEIR NICKNAMES

Eighteen French kings bore the name Louis. Give the number attached to the Louis known by each of the following nicknames.

1) The Father of His People
2) The Grand Monarch
3) The Pious, or the Debonaire
4) The Restoration King
5) Saint Louis
6) The Terrible King, or the Universal Spider
7) The Great, or The Sun King (*Le Roi Soleil*)
8) The Well-Beloved (*Le Bien-Aimé*)
9) The Lost Dauphin
10) Louis d'Outremer, or Louis from overseas

Answers:

1) (Louis) XII
2) (Louis) XIV
3) (Louis) I
4) (Louis) XVIII
5) (Louis) IX
6) (Louis) XI
7) (Louis) XIV
8) (Louis) XV
9) (Louis) XVII
10) (Louis) IV

AUTHORS AND THEIR FIRST NOVELS

Identify the author of each of the following first novels.

1) *Maggie: A Girl of the Streets*
2) *Sister Carrie*
3) *The Wapshot Chronicle*
4) *The Gilded Age*
5) *The Ox-Bow Incident*
6) *This Side of Paradise*
7) *Watch and Ward*
8) *The Man Within*
9) *Where Angels Fear to Tread*
10) *Windy McPherson's Son*

Answers:

1) Stephen Crane
2) Theodore Dreiser
3) John Cheever
4) Mark Twain
5) Walter van Tilburg Clark
6) F. Scott Fitzgerald
7) Henry James
8) Graham Greene
9) E(dward) M(organ) Forster
10) Sherwood Anderson

DATES OF MAJOR DISASTERS

Identify, within 5 years, the dates of each of the following major disasters.

1) Great London Fire
2) Lisbon earthquake
3) Johnstown, Pennsylvania, flood
4) Krakatoa explosion
5) San Francisco quake
6) Alaskan Earthquake
7) Mount Vesuvius eruption that destroyed Pompeii
8) Mount Pelée eruption in Martinique
9) Japan earthquake that destroyed one third of Tokyo and most of Yokohama
10) Tay Bridge disaster in Scotland

Answers:

1) 1666 (1661-1671)
2) 1755 (1750-1760)
3) 1889 (1884-1894)
4) 1883 (1878-1888)
5) 1906 (1901-1911)
6) 1964 (1959-1969)
7) A.D. 79 (74-84)
8) 1902 (1897-1907)
9) 1923 (1918-1928)
10) 1889 (1884-1994)

YEARS OF PRESIDENTIAL ELECTION SLOGANS

Identify the year in which each of the following political slogans was used in the U.S. presidential election.

1) Tippecanoe and Tyler Too
2) Tilden and Reform
3) A House Divided Against Itself Cannot Stand
4) Free Soil, Free Speech, Free Labor, and Free Men
5) Rum, Romanism, and Rebellion
6) The Moose is loose
7) We Want Willkie
8) Give 'Em Hell Harry
9) Extremism in the Pursuit of Liberty is No Vice
10) Are You Better Off than You Were Four Years Ago?

Answers:

1) 1840 (W.H. Harrison and M. van Buren)
2) 1876 (R.B. Hayes and S.J. Tilden)
3) 1860 (A. Lincoln and J. Breckinridge)
4) 1848 (Z. Taylor, L. Cass, M. van Buren)
5) 1884 (G. Cleveland and J. Blaine)
6) 1912 (W. Wilson, T. Roosevelt, W. Taft, and E. Debs)
7) 1940 (FDR and W. Willkie)
8) 1948 (H. Truman and T. Dewey)
9) 1964 (LBJ and B. Goldwater)
10) 1980 (R. Reagan and J. Carter)

U.S. CAPITALS

Identify the following U.S. capitals.

1) City named after an explorer and located on the Congaree River, just below the junction of the Broad and Saluda rivers
2) City in the foothills of the Sangre de Cristo Range of the Southern Rockies
3) City on the Missouri River near Big Bend Dam
4) City on the Delaware River with the motto "_______ Makes—the World Takes"
5) Arkansas River city known as the "City of Three Capitols"
6) County seat of Laramie County
7) City located about 25 miles from the Gulf of Mexico and named from the Creek for "Old Town"
8) City located at the base of the Sierra Nevada and near the Comstock Lode
9) City located near the Chattahoochee River and used as a Confederate supply depot during the Civil War
10) City originally named "La Petite Roche" by a French explorer

Answers:

1) Columbia
2) Santa Fe
3) Pierre
4) Trenton
5) Little Rock
6) Cheyenne
7) Tallahassee
8) Carson City
9) Atlanta
10) Little Rock

LUNGS AND BREATHING

Identify each of the following terms concerning lungs and breathing.

1) Temporary stopping of breathing, frequently caused by too much oxygen or too little carbon dioxide in the brain
2) To breathe hard with a whistling, raspy sound caused by mucus in the trachea or bronchial tubes
3) Thin membrane lining the thoracic or chest cavity covering the lungs
4) Infectious disease mainly affecting the lungs and once known as consumption
5) Lidlike opening of the larynx that automatically clamps shut when a person swallows
6) Openings in the nose through which air enters
7) Energy-producing process by which living organisms obtain and use oxygen
8) Thin wall of cartilage separating the openings in the nose
9) Inflammation of the thin membrane covering the lungs and lining the chest cavity
10) Device that measures the amount of air inhaled

Answers:

1) Apnea (or apnoea; accept asphyxia)
2) Wheeze
3) Pleura
4) Tuberculosis (also known as TB)
5) Epiglottis
6) Nostrils
7) Respiration
8) Septum
9) Pleurisy (pleuritis)
10) Spirometer (pulmometer and pneumatometer)

PHILOSOPHIES

Identify the philosophy characterized by each of the following.

1) Focuses on human beings, rather than on divine or supernatural concerns, and popular during the Renaissance
2) Denies possibility of discerning existence of God
3) Asserts that knowledge is gained only through experience, a belief advanced by Locke and Hume
4) Sees pleasure as the ultimate good
5) Denies the existence of God
6) Sees God as a creator only, assuming no later control over life
7) Sees the world divided into 2 fundamental types of substance, such as mind and matter or good and evil
8) Focuses on human isolation, holding that man has freedom of choice and must accept responsibility for that choice, as asserted by Soren Kierkegaard
9) Asserts that only physical matter is real and that everything can be explained in terms of physical laws
10) Involves belief in a single God

Answers:

1) Humanism
2) Agnosticism
3) Empiricism
4) Hedonism
5) Atheism
6) Deism (do NOT accept theism)
7) Dualism
8) Existentialism
9) Materialism
10) Monotheism (theism)

U.S. PRESIDENTS AND THEIR CABINETS

Identify each of the following concerning U.S. Presidents and their Cabinets.

1) One whose Cabinet officer, Elizabeth Dole, testified before a congressional panel chaired by her husband, Robert Dole
2) One who appointed Edmond Randolph as the youngest secretary of state
3) One whose secretary of state, Cordell Hull, won the Nobel Peace Prize
4) Only one who completed his term without making any changes in his Cabinet
5) One who reorganized his entire Cabinet over the Peggy Neale Eaton affair
6) Only one to appoint a relative to a Cabinet position, that of attorney general
7) One who appointed Alexander Hamilton as the youngest secretary of the Treasury
8) One whose secretary of the interior, Albert Fall, was the first Cabinet member ever jailed for a criminal act
9) One who appointed Carla Hills as the youngest secretary of Housing and Urban Development
10) One whose 6-man cabinet suggested in 1841 that he be designated as "Acting President"

Answers:

1) Ronald Reagan (Dole was the Secretary of Transportation and she appeared before the Senate Finance Committee)
2) George Washington (Randolph was 40 years old)
3) Franklin Roosevelt
4) Franklin Pierce
5) Andrew Jackson
6) John F. Kennedy (he appointed his brother Robert Kennedy)
7) George Washington (Hamilton was 32 years old)
8) Warren Harding (jailed in 1929; resigned his Cabinet post in 1923)
9) Jimmy Carter (Hills was 41 years old)
10) John Tyler (when he succeeded William Henry Harrison)

THE WORD *LIBERTY*

Identify each of the following associated with the word *liberty*.

1) Patriot who on March 23, 1775, said, "I know not what course others may take, but as for me, give me liberty or give me death."
2) Document with the words, ". . . all men are created equal, . . . with certain unalienable rights, that among these are life, liberty, and the pursuit of happiness."
3) Orator who concluded an 1830 speech with the words, "Liberty and Union, now and forever, one and inseparable!"
4) President whose inaugural address included the words, ". . . that we shall pay any price . . . to assure the survival and success of liberty."
5) President who said, "Fourscore and seven years ago our fathers brought forth on this continent, a new nation, conceived in liberty and . . ."
6) Andrew Jackson's Vice President, who said, "The Union, next to our liberty, the most dear!"
7) Country whose motto is translated as, "Liberty, Equality, Fraternity"
8) Arizona senator who said, "Extremism in the defense of liberty is no vice. . . ."
9) Document with the words, ". . . and to the Republic for which it stands, one Nation, under God, indivisible, with liberty and justice for all."
10) Song with the words: "My country, 'tis of thee, / Sweet land of liberty, / Of thee I sing."

Answers:

1) Patrick Henry
2) Declaration of Independence
3) Daniel Webster
4) John Kennedy
5) Abraham Lincoln
6) John C. Calhoun
7) France
8) Barry Goldwater
9) Pledge of Allegiance
10) "America" (by Samuel Francis Smith)

AFRICAN AMERICANS IN FICTION, DRAMA, AND AUTOBIOGRAPHY

Identify each of the following.

1) Nobel Prize author Toni Morrison's phantom character killed in infancy by her mother to keep her from being returned to slavery
2) "Mother of the Blues," the title character in August Wilson's _____ _____*'s Black Bottom* about blues as a response to oppression
3) Title character of Ernest Gaines' novel, called an autobiography, about Ticey, a slave later known as Jane, from Civil War to 1960s
4) Subject of *Black Boy*, which follows the author from his early years in Jim Crow South to adulthood in Chicago
5) Former slave foreman in *Gone With the Wind* who rescues Scarlett and is known for his line "Quittin' time at Tara"
6) Compassionate and enduring African-American cook on whom the 3rd section of Faulkner's *The Sound and the Fury* is focused
7) Slave who to avoid the sale of her son escapes to the North across the frozen Ohio River in Stowe's *Uncle Tom's Cabin*
8) Narrator of Zora Neale Hurston's *Their Eyes Were Watching God*, who rejects materialism and status to follow her own instincts
9) Son who wants to use insurance money to buy a liquor store rather than suburban home his mother wants in Hansberry's *A Raisin in the Sun*
10) Surname of the civil rights leader who struggles to find her identity in Alice Walker's book *Meridian*

Answers:

1) Beloved
2) Ma Rainey
3) Jane Pittman (Jane Brown)
4) Richard Wright
5) Big Sam
6) Dilsey
7) Eliza (Harris)
8) Janie (Crawford)
9) Walter Lee Younger
10) (Meridian) Hill

INDEX BY TITLE

INDEX BY SUBJECT